A Guide to Mushrooms

A Guide to Mushrooms

*The Edible and Poisonous Fungi
of the Northern Hemisphere*

Michael Jordan B.Sc., M.Inst.Biol.

millington

For my son, Stephen.

First published 1975 by
Millington Ltd.
109 Southampton Row
London WC1B 4HH

Printed in Italy by Librex S.p.A.

Contents

Acknowledgements

I am indebted to the following institutions and individuals for their kind and generous assistance in compiling certain sections of this book:

The Department of Cryptogamic Botany, Museum of Natural History, London.
The University of London Central Periodical Library.
Mr T. G. Denham of W. Darlington and Sons Ltd (mushroom growers).
Dr C. J. Toynton of the Princess Elizabeth Hospital, Guernsey.
Mr and Mrs M. J. le Cocq, for permission to detail their personal case histories in connection with *A. phalloides* poisoning.
Miss Pat Baker for advice on fungus cookery.

I owe a particular debt of gratitude to Alan Wrangles, whose patient guidance and criticism have been invaluable in learning the new, and often bewildering, accomplishment of writing a book.

Many other people will recognise small details for which they were responsible; these are too numerous to list but are gratefully acknowledged.

Introduction

Today, fungus–hunting attracts an ever–increasing number of enthusiasts, but it is worth remembering that our Victorian forbears paved the way to much of our present knowledge of fungi, and nowhere with such dedication and often personal risk as in assessing the culinary value or danger of different species.

Several volumes are currently available to assist the amateur mycologist with identification in the field. Until now, however, there has been an absence of any reliable guide to the poisonous and edible varieties, and many people still hold erroneous belief in the old maxim: 'mushrooms good—toadstools bad'.

This book sets out firmly to disprove the myths and fallacies, by giving detailed descriptions of all the poisonous and edible fungi that one is likely to encounter in the field. Most of these descriptions are accompanied by colour photographs of the fungi, taken as they were found in their natural settings, so providing a reliable basis on which to make accurate identification.

The fruiting bodies, or sporophores, of Higher Fungi generally appear in the autumn, though some can be found throughout the year and a few are vernal, or spring species. The vegetative part of the fungus is present throughout the year, under the ground or substratum, as a cotton–wool like network of threads or hyphae, called the mycelium.

Providing the habitat listed for a given species is present they can be found growing almost anywhere geographically, as long as conditions of temperature and ground moisture are adequate for development of the mycelium and the 'germination' of the sporophores.

In the northern hemisphere Higher Fungi extend in range from Siberia to the Mediterranean, and from the western seaboard of America to eastern Asia. They can be found growing on mountain-sides and moorlands, woods, fields, riverbanks, city parks, even under the floorboards of your home.

Glossary

aculeate: having narrow spines
adnate: (of tubes or gills) widely joined to the stipe
adnexed: (of tubes or gills) narrowly joined to the stipe
adpressed: closely flattened down
alutaceous: colour of leather
annulus: ring–like partial veil, or remnants of it, round stipe after expansion of pileus
arcuate: arc–like
areolate: having division by cracks into small areas
attenuate: narrowing
caespitose: in joined groups or tufts
campanulate: bell–like in form
capillitium: a mass of sterile, thread–like tubes or fibres among the spores
capitulum: globose fertile head in some fungi including *Claviceps*
cavernose: having large cavities in the tissue
clavate: club–like in form, either narrowing to the top or the base
connate: joined together at birth or during development
convex: equally rounded
coriaceous: leather–like in texture
cortina: fine, cobwebby veil (eg. in *Cortinarius* and *Inocybe* spp.)
crenate: having margin decorated with rounded teeth
crenulate: slightly crenate in form
cuticle: outer layer of compressed hyphae
decurrent: (of tubes or gills) running down the stipe
dentate: toothed
denticulate: having small teeth
disc: (of a pileus) central part of the top surface
distal: situated towards margin or periphery of a body

distant:	gills widely spaced apart
echinate:	having sharply pointed spines
ellipsoidal:	having the shape of an ellipse
endo–peridium:	inner layer of peridium
exo–peridium:	outer layer of peridium
farinose:	meal–like in form or smell
fibrillar:	consisting of fibres
fibrillose:	covered with silky or fine fibres
filiform:	thread–like in form
flexuose:	undulating or crooked
floccose:	cottony in texture or appearance
free:	(of tubes or gills) not fixed to the stipe
frondose:	bearing broad leaf–like leaves typical of Angiosperm trees, as opposed to needle–like leaves of Conifers
fugaceous:	having a short existence
fulvous:	pale tawny brown colour
fuscous:	dusky brown colour
fusiform:	spindle–like in form
glabrous:	not hairy
gleba:	spore–producing tissue of Gasteromycetes and Tuberales
glutinous:	sticky but dull
gregarious:	in companies or groups but not joined together
hyaline:	more or less transparent, without colour
hygrophanous:	having a water–logged appearance when wet
hymenium:	the spore bearing layer of a sporophore
imbricate:	(of pilei) overlapping like tiles on a roof
involute:	(of a pileus) with the edge rolled under or in
infundibuliform:	funnel–like in form
lacunose:	having holes or cavities
ligulate:	strap–like in form, flat and narrow
lobate:	having small lobes
μ:	= 1 micron = one thousandth of a millimetre (0.001mm)
pallid:	light coloured, pale
papillate:	adorned with small rounded processes
pellicle:	delicate outer membrane
pedestal:	basal supporting region of some sporophores (eg. *Clavaria* and *Lycoperdon*, typically sterile)
peridium:	wall or limiting membrane of a sporangium or other fruit body
pileus:	cap of a fungus, bearing tubes, gills etc
piriform:	pear–like in shape
plane:	flat
plicate:	folded in pleats
proximal:	situated towards the centre or axis of a body
pruinose:	flour–like or frosty covering on a surface
pulvinate:	cushion–like in form

punctate:	marked with very small spots or hollows
reniform:	kidney–like in form
resupinate:	(of sporophores) flat on the substratum, with hymenium outwards
revolute:	(of a pileus) with the edge rolled back or up
rimose:	fibres of cuticle parted showing underlying tissue (eg. in *Inocybe* spp.)
rufescent:	tending towards rufous colour
rufous:	brownish red colour
rugose:	roughly wrinkled
sclerotium:	a firm, often rounded mass of hyphae with or without addition of host tissue, normally having no spores in or on it
scrobiculate:	finely pitted with small depressions
sessile:	lacking a stipe
sinuate:	(of tubes or gills) having a sudden curve near the stipe
spathulate:	spoon–like in form
spinulose:	having delicate spines
spore:	typically one–celled reproductive structure in Cryptogams
sporophore:	spore producing or spore bearing structure
squamule:	small scale
squamulose:	adorned with small scales
squarrose:	adorned with reflexed squamules
stipe:	stalk of a fungal sporophore bearing the pileus
stipitate:	having a stipe
striate:	marked with fine lines
strigose:	having obvious coarse hairs
stroma (pl. stromata):	a mass of vegetative hyphae with or without host or substratum tissue
stuffed:	(of a stipe) having the inside tissue of a different texture than the outer layer
subdistant:	relating to gills, between crowded and wholly distant
sulcate:	grooved
tomentose:	having a covering of soft, typically matted, downy hairs
umbilicate:	having a small hollow at the disc
umbo:	boss–like protuberance at the disc
umbonate:	having an umbo
velar:	pertaining to veil or velum
ventricose:	having a swelling in the middle or at one side
verrucose:	having small wart–like processes
villose:	covered with long, soft, unmatted hairs
viscid:	slimy or wet, shining, sticky
volva:	cup–like lower part of a universal veil, round the base of a mature stipe in certain Agarics including *Amanita* spp.

SECTION THROUGH
GENERALISED HELVELLA

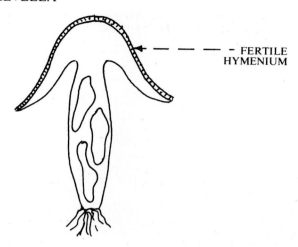

FERTILE
HYMENIUM

SECTION THROUGH
GENERALISED MOREL

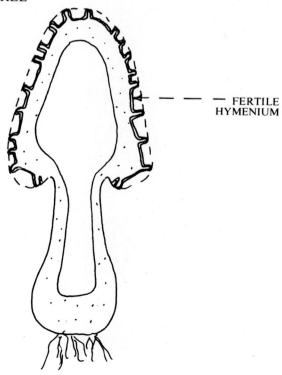

FERTILE
HYMENIUM

SECTION THROUGH GENERALISED AGARIC

(in *Boletus* spp. pores replace gills)

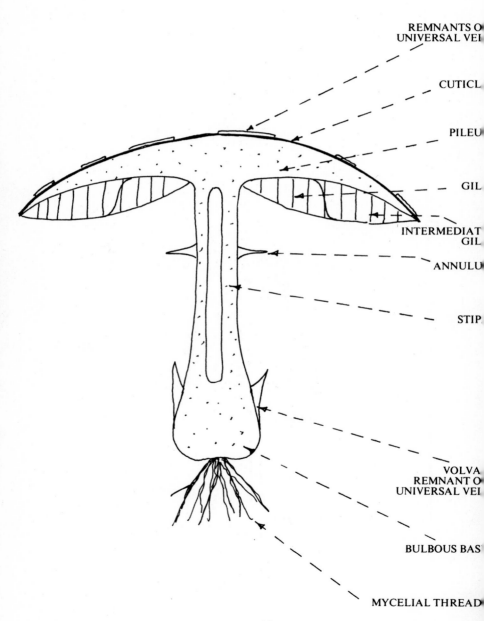

REMNANTS O
UNIVERSAL VEI

CUTICL

PILEU

GIL

INTERMEDIAT
GIL

ANNULU

STIP

VOLVA
REMNANT O
UNIVERSAL VEI

BULBOUS BAS

MYCELIAL THREAD

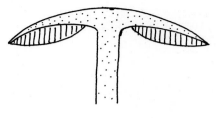

FREE

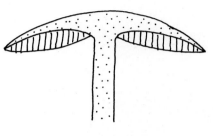

ADNEXED

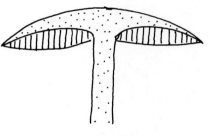

ADNATE

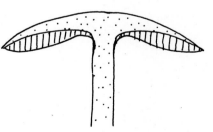

SINUATE

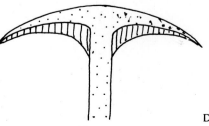

DECURRENT

SECTION THROUGH
GENERALISED 'PUFF BALL'
GASTEROMYCETE

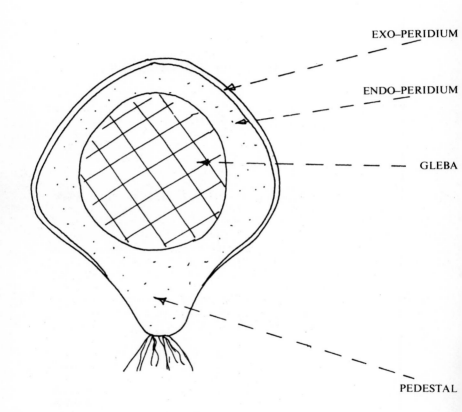

EXO–PERIDIUM

ENDO–PERIDIUM

GLEBA

PEDESTAL

CHAPTER ONE

Mushrooms and Toadstools

Through the centuries, since man first began to take an intelligent view of the potential foodstuffs at his disposal, the edibility of fungi has been the subject of a great many erroneous beliefs. Even in the light of modern experience, they are some of the most grossly maligned inhabitants of this planet, and it is unfortunately true that much of this can be ascribed to plain ignorance.

Most of the lore about fungi is based purely on superstition. Some of the associations which have grown up about fungi do, of course, have a thread of fact running through them, and these are undoubtedly attributable to the limited number of varieties which do have medicinal properties, be they benign or otherwise. On the whole, however, fungi are inoffensive plants, not only doing a useful scavenging operation on the earth's rubbish, but also here and there providing enjoyable foods. The time has long passed when *Homo sapiens* was merely content to stuff nutrients into his belly so as to ward off the effects of hunger; in all civilised societies, the eating of food has taken on a subsidiary quality of artistic enjoyment.

No longer is food merely to be obtained and consumed. A whole modern industry has built up geared to the rendering of foodstuffs positively attractive to the eye and the palate. Thus, any ingredient which can be effectively employed to enhance the otherwise bland or over–familiar taste of our more staple foods is welcome. Many fungi can effectively fulfil this role by providing unusual and stimulating flavours.

The pioneers in the use of the exotic or the unusual in the kitchen were the ancient civilisations of the Greeks, the Romans and the Chinese, who developed their own parallel but wholly independent cookery. However, although the present–day, almost ubiquitous, spread of the Chinese restaurant now brings Oriental flavours to us, we are far more familiar with the ways of Roman cookery, and it is certain that much of our present culinary lore has stemmed from the influence of the Roman occupation.

It is therefore to the patricians of imperial Rome that one must look for the origins of fungus cookery in western society.

The Sicilian physician and herbalist, Dioscorides, had this to say of fungi in the second century AD:

'Fungi have a twofold difference, for they are either good for food or poisonous; their poisonous nature depends on various causes, for either such fungi grow amongst rusty nails or rotten rags, or near serpents' holes, or on trees producing noxious fruits; such have a thick coating of mucus, and when laid by after being gathered, quickly become putrid; but others, not of this kind, impart a sweet taste to sauces. However even these, if partaken of too freely, are injurious, being indigestible, causing stricture or cholera. As a safeguard, all should be eaten with a draught of olive oil, or soda and lye ashes with salt and vinegar, and a decoction of savory or marjoram, or they should be followed with a draught composed of birds' dung and vinegar, or with a linctus of much honey; for even the edible sorts are difficult of digestion, and generally pass whole with the excrement.' (transl. Houghton 1885)

Hilarious as this account may seem, it is not quite so far fetched as it first appears. The liberal application of olive oil to ensure no 'hold ups on the way through' was quite sensible, if not particularly appetising, advice generally echoed by physicians until much later times. Oil was a favourite dressing for all sorts of vegetable dishes, and its use seems to have stimulated predictable results. Cicero, having attended a dinner given by the augures of the House of Lentulus, which included extensive vegetarian dishes, was said to have been seized with such violent diarrhoea for ten days that he was hardly able to stand (Buller).

The poisonous factor in certain fungi is of an acid nature. For example, the saddle fungi (*Helvella* spp.) synthesise helvellic acid, which has a discomforting effect on most individuals, and the ancients had great faith in the neutralising properties of bird dung, which has a high alkaline content. Since most households kept domestic fowl, collection of raw material was quite convenient, though it was considered that the dung of a free range bird was much better than that of one in confinement.

Conversely, many of the worst fungal toxins fall into the class of compounds known as alkaloids. These all have a pronounced action on body physiology and are basic in chemical characteristic. This is probably where the use of vinegar (weak acetic acid) came in, because dilute tannic acid (as in tea) is still used in the treatment of some alkaloid poisoning. It reacts with the alkaloid, turning it into a relatively harmless, insoluble compound, and acetic acid may have similar effect on a number of poisons.

The first adverse manifestations of some poisonous varieties are burning sensations of the mouth and tongue and choking in the throat, for which a strong honey linctus would naturally be soothing.

One cannot help feeling, however, that all these delightful condiments would rather have detracted from the joy of eating the fungi, so why did the Romans bother? There may be a number of possible explanations, apart from the effect of sheer boredom. Towards the end of the Roman Republic, when all good patricians were expected to 'tighten their belts', the Senate passed sumptuary laws, which included a ban on the use of certain costly or extravagant meat dishes. There was, however, no restriction on the use of vegetables (presumably to encourage Romans to grow their own), and one entertaining diversion in a rather gloomy diet was fungi.

The practice of eating untried and, wherever possible, exotic foods was something the Romans seized on with gusto. Although they tackled their unknown fungi with some degree of caution, they nevertheless experimented fairly extensively—a practice which no doubt accounted for many a bereavement.

The terminology which the Romans used for different kinds of fungus is not always easy to follow, as some of their original 'tags' now have quite different meanings.

They distinguished between 'fungi farnei' (tree fungi), which were presumably those growing on or around trees; 'boleti' which were not the present day pore bearing fungi, but gill bearing agarics, growing on soil; 'suilli', which were the true pore bearing fungi, now referred to as Boletae; and truffles, the subterranean tuberous fungi which have achieved great popularity in many European countries.

Amanita caesaria, a species which does not grow in the British Isles, was one of the most popular 'boleti' among the Roman Emperors, as its name implies. Its range extends through the southern part of Europe and the southern United States, and until quite recent times it could often be seen during the autumn dis—played for sale in markets in cities like Milan and Bologna.

A. caesaria was a favourite of the celebrated Roman gourmet Apicus, who lived at the time of the Emperor Tiberius. Apicus compiled a manual of cookery which has survived to the present day, and one finds many references in it to the use of fungi.

The ritual that went with fungus eating was sometimes a little elaborate—special vessels called boletaria were reserved for cooking fungi, and woe betide any servant of a Roman house—hold who used the boletarium for inferior purposes. The satirist of the day, Martial, made a topical quip: 'although boleti have given me so noble a name, I am now used, I am ashamed to say, for Brussels sprouts'. (transl. Houghton 1885).

The Romans tended to prefer food heavily spiced and sauced (in common with much medieval English cookery), presumably because of the difficulties in keeping any food fresh, which resulted in the necessity to disguise some rather off—putting tastes and smells!

Thus 'fungi farnei' were generally boiled and then strained dry to be served with copious amounts of pepper and a condiment called liquamen. Salt as a commodity was scarce in imperial Rome, and liquamen was liberally used as a substitute. The recipe included such tasty ingredients as fish guts! A forerunner of Worcester sauce no doubt!

17

'Boleti', on the other hand, were traditionally cooked in caroenum, a sauce made with wine which has been boiled down to a stronger concentration.

Elsewhere in Europe and Asia, fungi have been eaten to a limited extent, though much more extensively in France, where their popularity has rivalled that in Italy.

The Greeks also certainly made extensive use of fungi in their cooking, but I think that less work has been done on extracting and translating their recipes than in the case of the Roman culture.

A fascinating insight into the popularity of eating fungi on the Continent was provided by a special bill passed in Italy in 1837. The government was seriously concerned about the number of deaths which were resulting from the unrestricted sale of fungi over a number of years. A special committee, the Congregazione Speciale di Sanita, was set up to work out legislative safeguards, and it came up with the following rules:

1. That for the future, an Inspector of Funguses, versed in Botany, be appointed to attend the market in place of a peasant whose supposed practical knowledge had hitherto been held as sufficient guarantee for the public safety.

2. That all fungi brought into Rome by the different gates be registered, under the surveillance of the Principal Officer, in whose presence the baskets be sealed up, and the whole day's consumption be sent under escort to a central depot.

3. That a particular place be fixed on for the fungus market and that hawking elsewhere in the streets be forbidden under penalty of fine or imprisonment.

4. That at 7.0 a.m. precisely the Inspector should examine the fungi, spread out on the ground. A printed permission of sale was to be issued, on payment of one baioccho (0.2 pence) per 10 lb for approved fungi.

5. That quantities of less than 10 lb be free of tax.

6. That the stale fungi of the previous day, as well as mouldy or maggoty specimens, together with any specimen of the 'common mushroom' found in the baskets, be sent under escort and thrown into the Tiber.

7. That the Inspector be empowered to fine or imprison any who infringed the above regulations; finally that he furnish a weekly report regarding the sales of fungi, to the Tribunal of Provisions (Pilât).

I have come across one tragically funny sequel to this elaborate arrangement. There was at one time a comparable system organised in France, but one of the first Parisian fungus inspectors, supposedly well versed in the different varieties, apparently died shortly after taking up the post. Cause of death? Fungus poisoning.

The reference in the Italian legislation to 'common mushroom' is something of a mystery. Our familiar *Agaricus bisporus* and its field brethren were not viewed at all kindly in Italy, and one can only speculate that this was on account of the possible mistaken identity with *Amanita phalloides*. It is known that this deadly fungus was frequently mistaken for the 'common mushroom' (and still is), and the reason for such an incomprehensible ruling may lie there.

Undoubtedly the experimentation of the ancient civilizations and their quaint superstitions have been the trigger for much of the fungal lore that has been carried down through the centuries, so what of the worth of fungi in light of modern experience?

Many of the misconceptions about edible fungi which have germinated in the British Isles are probably to be blamed on using the cultivated, shop–bought mushrooms as a yardstick. Unlike many European countries which tend to have traditional recipes for a variety of fungi, our own experience is largely restricted to *Agaricus campestris* (and its cultivated counterparts), and in the Midland counties, to *Lepista nuda* and *Lepista saeva*, the blewits.

We therefore tend to base our immediate assessment of a strange fungus on whether it looks, feels, and smells like a mushroom. In fact all sorts of weird and wonderful old–wives–tales have arisen concerning safe 'tests' for fungi, all of which are totally unfounded. There is only one real basis for selection, and that is experience.

It is worth detailing the fallacious ideas, if only to dispose of them fully:

Edible fungi reputedly 'peel' whilst poisonous varieties do not. Unfortunately both the edible field mushroom and the lethally poisonous death cap *(Amanita phalloides)* share this distinction.

Poisonous fungi reputedly blacken a silver spoon which is dipped into the juices during cooking, whilst edible fungi produce no reaction—this idea probably stems from the theory, once widely held, that silver will draw poisonous substances out of an object with which it is in contact and absorb them. However, to cite two extreme instances again, neither the field mushroom nor the 'death cap' induce any reaction at all with a silver spoon.

If the specimen is eaten by other animals, it is supposed to be suitable for human fare—an extremely hazardous assumption, because the death cap, to name but one dangerous specimen, is eaten with apparent immunity by a variety of animals including rabbits.

Brightly coloured fungi are considered unwholesome, whilst neutral looking specimens are supposed to be edible. This is quite untrue, and although some brightly coloured specimens are indeed poisonous, others, looking remarkably like a field mushroom at first glance, also share that distinction.

If the cut flesh changes colour, the fungus is also considered to be suspect. This is a totally unfounded idea, doubtless emanating from the misconception of poisonous substances being dark, or reacting to the light.

Having disposed of the more widely known fallacies, it is

time to look at the practical aspects of collecting and cooking fungi.

The great majority of Higher Fungi are harmless if eaten, but many of them are not suitable to be used as food, quite simply because they are unpalatable. This is not to imply that they are poisonous, but that they lack the taste, or a suitable texture, to make an enjoyable meal. A tough, woody bracket fungus can be cooked in any number of different ways, and it will probably still be tough and woody at the end of the process; likewise, whatever one tries to do with *Boletus felleus,* a close relative of the delicious, edible cep fungus, the odds are that it will remain obnoxiously bitter and unwholesome.

The point I stress, however, is that should the fungus gourmet inadvertently include one such 'rogue' specimen with his dinner, he will not be violently ill, nor experience hallucinations, nor have convulsions. With many species he will probably not even notice the error, and at the most the dish will be tainted with an unpleasant taste.

Putting aside this great bulk of harmless specimens, one is then left with two relatively small groups which lie at opposite ends of the gastronomic scale: the poisonous varieties and the edible varieties.

In the British Isles, there are some one hundred species of Higher Fungi that have become recognised through centuries of painful trial and error as being not only safe to eat but also good to eat. I think a word or two is justifiable here on the subject of the nutrient value of fungi, about which there are again numerous conflicting tales.

One day we may be faced with the unwelcome prospect of a future in which fungus is a staple diet. Although of relatively low protein content per fresh weight, fungi have been proved to be rich in other nutritional requirements. These include vitamins of the B group, such as pantothenic acid, and niacin, as well as vitamin C (ascorbic acid), all of which are quite well retained in either cooking or drying.

It is an interesting point that during his explorations in HMS *Beagle*, Charles Darwin discovered a tribe of Fuegans in the extreme tip of South America, apparently unique in their use of fungus as a staple diet. The area is very barren and inhospitable, having an atrocious climate, and other than a few hardy berries and lichens the only real vegetation growing there is a species of evergreen beech. The Fuegans long ago discovered a disc–like fungus grew in reasonable quantity on the beech throughout the year. On experimentation, they found it to be palatable and came to rely on it more or less entirely as a source of vegetable diet. Darwin appropriately named the fungus *Cyttaria Darwinii.*

Should the major populations of the world need to look to fungi as a basic source of food, it is unlikely to be in the form of the familiar edible mushroom or any of its allies, because although relative to its dry weight fungal tissue is actually rich in protein, the average mushroom contains about 98% water. Thus, every kilo of mushrooms picked and consumed will only offer the same nutrient value as an inch square cube of cheese, and vast quantities would be needed to provide the necessary calorific value for daily sustenance.

The answer to our future table fare in a world rapidly running out of sources of food may well lie with yeasts, fungi of the Ascomycete group which not only grow with incredible speed but also lack the very high water content of many other fungi.

It is a known fact that prisoners of war have supplemented starvation diets by scraping yeasts from the walls of buildings, and using part of their food allowance to make them grow, since the yeast rapidly exceeded the weight and nutrient value of the original 'culture medium'.

CHAPTER TWO

Preparations for the Table

Cooking fungi must surely be one of the most delightful excursions through the realm of culinary art. A whole new experience of flavour, texture and bouquet is available—at very little expense—to anyone who cares to take the opportunity.

I can think of few more refreshing ways of spending a fine Sunday afternoon in autumn than to wend a lazy path through mellow woods and pick these fascinating plants; there is great satisfaction in carrying home a basket full of blewits, boleti, or whatever else takes your fancy, safe in the knowledge that your meal will not have been deluged with chemicals, nor deep frozen, nor factory processed.

I am ashamed to recall that my own tentative début in the cooking of fungi was both cowardly and unspectacular; my accoutrements for the preparation of each succulent dish were a knife, a saucepan, and a knob of butter; my recipe was an unwavering sauté for five minutes, toss in some salt and pepper, and hope for the best; it was some time before I became daredevil enough to extend my epicurean adventures to such risque condiments as lemon juice or cider.

In retrospect though, I think it was probably not a bad way to start, because it taught me at first hand the basic culinary virtues of a lot of strange foods that the book of reference seemed invariably to describe in such enlightening terms as 'edible and good', or even 'some find indigestible'—a phrase which at one time would have had me washing my hands with feverish attention after merely touching the specimen to which it referred.

I gnawed my way through the stalks of *Lepiota* parasols; I swallowed crisp specks that had once been elegant chanterelles; I conducted dental battles with india–rubber lumps of oyster cap. I enjoyed the experience enormously, and I am sure it served to place in true perspective some of the more exotic and elaborate recipes for fungi, many of which I can't help feeling are pretty much a waste of time, since they quite overwhelm the delicate virtues of the specimens so industriously collected.

What, therefore, is really needed in the way of equipment for a fungus collecting trip?

All that one basically requires (other than the book of words) is a sharp knife and a flat collecting basket of the trug type; once a fungus is bruised (in common with most vegetables) it will deteriorate much faster than if handled with care and allowed to reach the kitchen undamaged.

Collecting fungi into polythene bags is not to be recommended, because they tend to exclude air from the specimens and condensation rapidly builds up in the bag. If the air is damp or warm to any degree (particularly in the car on the way home) the fungi can quickly go stale and mushy. Whenever possible pick the specimens by pulling them up from the soil, intact. Sometimes this is not practical—for example, with an oyster cap (*Pleurotius ostreatus*) it is considerably hard work to try to pull it off the tree trunk—in which case the stalk should be cut, cleanly, as near the base as possible.

Place all the specimens gills upwards in the basket, having first carefully inspected them for maggots or other imperfections. The caps should preferably be arranged in a single layer, but frankly, unless one loads oneself with an enormous collecting basket, this may not always be practical. So, if it is convenient, return to the car to dispose of one basketful, without trying to cram layer upon layer, before collecting any more; otherwise, the specimens underneath may be disappointingly spoilt.

Incidentally, as it is well nigh impossible to extricate dirt from between the gills, it is advisable to brush off any surplus soil before inverting the caps—there is nothing more off–putting than a gritty toadstool in your mouth.

Once the specimens are collected it is desirable to transport them home as quickly as possible. There may be great temptation to snatch up all the likely looking toadstools at the beginning of a foray, on the theory that they won't be there when you come back. However, it is better to risk a slightly smaller crop than to tote a basketful of tired–looking specimens around the woods all day, because the resultant 'spread' on the kitchen table will invariably look sadly bedraggled compared with the fine juicy caps you first collected.

Then is the time to be finally selective about which specimens to retain and which to discard. The woodland floor is not always the ideal place to pick and choose. As often as not you may be tempted to gather a clump of honey fungus or a patch of blewits without too much concern for the finer points of each individual specimen, particularly if the rest of the party is anxious to keep moving or the family dog is doing his best to excavate the exact spot where your prize specimens have been located.

Discard any but the young, clean, healthy–looking fungi; that is not to say one needs go hunting around for 'buttons'—it is quite in order to use specimens with fully expanded caps—but it will soon become easy to distinguish a fungus in its prime with one that is past its best.

Shrivelled or soggy appearance, unwholesome odour, very deep colouring, or badly stained gills are all symptoms of fungi that have gone 'over the top' and are therefore strongly suspect for eating. Do remember that many edible fungi will not have the 'feel' of a mushroom; for example, many beginners are put off by the repellent rubberiness of the oyster cap, or the spongy feel of boleti, or the thick white spore dusting on a honey fungus. There is no need to be deterred by these things; after all, many of our common vegetables have quite distinctive and individual appearances which familiarity leads us happily to accept. Providing the specimens are properly cooked, all will be well by the time they reach the table.

Since theoretically one is discarding any specimens that appear dusty or dirty, there should be no need to wash them. However, in these days of widespread use of chemicals on agricultural land and roadside verges, it is just as well to give the fungi a rinse. The ideal way to go about this is first to cut off and discard the soiled base of the stem, and then to rinse each specimen singly in a sink full of warm water, with a final rinse under the tap. Dry gently on a tea towel before cooking.

Very few toadstools need peeling, and unless there is a specific reference to the need for this in the text, I would not recommend it. The practice spoils the appearance, probably removes some of the flavour and certainly does nothing to enhance the edibility of the specimens. The only real exception is when the cap has become dirty as a result of pushing its way up through soil and roots, or when it is particularly tough or viscid.

There are some instances where the stalks are too tough to make good eating, but in general stalks should be incorporated in the dish. If they are particularly large, it is advisable to cut each one lengthways in halves or quarters. Where the stalks should be discarded, reference is made in the text.

Before turning to the subject of cooking, there are various ways of keeping fungi, should one wish to do so. Invariably I seem to collect far more than I can eat at a sitting, and it always seems a terrible waste to throw the unused specimens on the rubbish heap.

Most types will keep for a couple of days in the fridge. The best container is a polythene tub with a self-sealing lid. Ensure that the specimens are not damp on the outside, and always inspect them carefully before finally using them. Creepy-crawlies are not deterred in the least by the chilly conditions of a fridge.

Talking to a Home Economics teacher about the subject of preservation, I discovered that I was sadly out-of-date on techniques and was surprised to learn that mushrooms can be satisfactorily deep frozen these days. Although I have not personally tried this out I must include the suggestion as a more long-term storage technique. I would suggest, though, that the method is better suited to the firmer and drier varieties.

There are several other ways of keeping fungi over long periods. One of them is drying, at which the Chinese are said to be pastmasters. Several varieties lend themselves particularly to this treatment. On the Continent the cep *(Boletus edulis)* is generally marketed dried, and the fairy ring champignon *(Maras-mius oreades)* is worth storing like this. Quite a lot of edible fungi are unsuitable for drying, because they 'go off' too rapidly, like *Boletus luteus,* or because they shrivel up in such a way that they will not effectively reconstitute at a later date. Where specimens are unsuitable for drying, the point is brought out in the text.

The best way of drying toadstools, and probably the simplest, is to thread them on coarse cotton with a darning needle and hang the string in an airing cupboard or some other warm, dry place. The dried caps will become quite unrecognisable, turning into little crisp specks, but don't be put off, because both the shape and texture can be brought back. Various methods of reconstituting are advocated, but having tried it myself, I have reached the con-clusion that an old Chinese method is still best—soak the dried caps in lukewarm water for five minutes, then transfer them to really hot water for half an hour, as if you were blanching.

Toadstools preserved thus should keep for some months, but it is advisable to store the strings sealed in a perfectly dry polythene container in a cool place.

A further extension of the drying idea is to put the dried caps through a blender (if, like me, you don't have one, it's back to the chopping board); the powder stores well and, if you select the right species, can effectively be employed in soups and stews. It is no good, however, attempting to use varieties with weak or even moderate flavour in this way, because taste and aroma will tend to be masked by the other ingredients of the dish. However, some of the really strong–flavoured varieties that are in them-selves too potent to use alone are ideal for powdering. Some suggestions to start off with are the 'fragrant agaric' *(Clitocybe odora),* or *Galerina mutabilis.*

In some English country districts, mushrooms are still pickled, and some worthwhile results can come from concocting a mixed preserve of surplus toadstools in this manner. The method is very easy and requires little additional material.

Place the caps and stalks into hot water for five minutes to blanch, and then mix with them about twice their own weight of small peeled onions (it may be necessary to chop the fungi into convenient sizes). Pack into a large earthenware or glass jar and cover with vinegar (you may also like to add some pickling spices); seal the container and store.

A variation on the pickling theme is mushroom ketchup. This is a particularly good way of using up autodigesting fungi, including *Coprinus* spp., because they tend to 'mush' of their own accord. However, most varieties other than the really firm ones will lend themselves to this process. Cut up the caps and stalks into smallish pieces and place them in an earthenware jar. Lightly sift salt over the layer, cover the jar, and stand it in a warm dark place, such as the airing cupboard or by the boiler. As surplus specimens are collected through the season, add these in layers, remembering to add the light dusting of salt between each 'picking'. Press down well at each stage. The caps soon degenerate to a delicious smelling mush.

When the jar is full, leave for a week and then turn out the contents into a large saucepan. Boil gently for half an hour, and then rub the mixture through a fine sieve with a wooden spoon. Add ½ oz. mixed pickling spices for each pint of liquid and return to the heat for twenty minutes, boiling vigorously. Strain the ketchup through a fine sieve into sterilised bottles and seal immediately.

Since the end of the last war, the salting down of vegetables for the winter has become something of a lost art, but it does offer another good way of using up the surplus stock from a collecting spree, and the result will guarantee a talking point among friends, when the intriguing jar is set out on the table with sausages or hamburgers! There is only one problem—the delicate mushroom aroma, which is well retained through the pickling process, is quickly lost once the bottle is opened. So, it is just as well to store in small–size bottles and, once opened, to use the contents as soon as possible.

What of cooking? One has only to walk into the nearest public library and to look through the cookery shelves to be over–whelmed with recipes for mushrooms. Sadly, though, you will rarely find much written about ways of serving other fungi. I feel certain, however, that the best maxim is to cook toadstools any way you wish to cook them. They are extremely versatile vegetables and will stand up gallantly to most of the experiments that you may care to try out.

One or two guidelines. Unless you are very sure that the species you select do not cause indigestion when eaten raw, don't use fungi fresh in salads. You may be sorely tempted to incorporate slices of blewit cap in this way because of its attractive colour, but here is an example of an excellent edible fungus that does contain minute amounts of a harmful substance until it is cooked.

It is also as well to bear in mind that fungi vary widely from the cultivated mushroom in strength of flavour. In many the flavour is so delicate that it can easily be smothered by other ingredients. On the other hand, some of the specimens listed have very strong flavours which would probably be unpalatable if the fungi were incorporated in a dish of their own. Only one or two caps of these need be added to a dish of milder fungi, or to be used as a condiment with soups, stews, or casseroles.

Another good way of tempering the flavour of some of the stronger varieties is to make a white sauce incorporating all or part of the juice derived from stewing the fungi, and then to pour this over the cooked specimens.

26

The size of the specimen is no great criterion, but when considering flavour it is as well to remember that fungi tend to become richer in flavour as they mature.

In the text I have offered a number of suggestions for the preparation of specific types, largely based on traditional recipes both English and Continental. However, here are some simple suggestions which can be applied generally to fungus cooking. (I have used the word 'mushroom' in all cases here, in deference to convention, which seems not unreasonable, since it is the word I am sure most people would prefer to think of when cooking fungi.)

Cream of mushroom soup

½ lb. mushrooms finely chopped

1½ pts. milk

⅓ pt. double cream

1 level tbs. flour

1 small onion finely chopped

seasoning

1 oz. butter

Melt the butter in a saucepan, and carefully mix in the flour; add the milk, stirring constantly to avoid lumps; add the chopped mushrooms and onions, season and cook over a low flame for 20 minutes stirring constantly; when thickened, pour in the cream and heat through.

This basic recipe can be seasoned to taste. For a slightly different flavour, the onions can be gently sautéed in the butter, before adding the flour. (serves 4)

Cold mushroom consommé

$\frac{1}{2}$ lb. mushrooms

$\frac{1}{2}$ pt. stock

cucumber

seasoning

lemon

Liquidise the mushrooms, and simmer for 20 minutes with the stock; strain through a sieve; allow to cool and add small diced pieces of cucumber for decoration, with lemon juice and seasoning to taste.

An excellent idea on a warm evening in late summer for some of the stronger flavoured species. (serves 2–3)

Mushroom hors d'oeuvres

(*Caution:* the species selected for this recipe must be suitable for eating uncooked.)

$\frac{1}{2}$ lb. mushrooms sliced

1 pt. prawn cocktail sauce

sliced lettuce leaves

cayenne pepper

Put the sliced lettuce in the bottom of individual, stemmed dishes; add the sliced mushrooms and pour over the cocktail sauce; sprinkle with cayenne pepper.

28

Mushrooms Italian

4 oz. mushrooms

8 oz. spaghetti

8 large tomatoes, or large can Italian plum tomatoes

2 small green peppers

spring onions

olives

juice of a lemon

2 tbs. olive oil

parsley and seasoning

Cook the spaghetti until tender; slice mushrooms, peppers, onions, and tomatoes, and cook rapidly for 3 minutes only, either in juice from canned tomatoes, or with a very small amount of water to prevent burning. Drain the spaghetti and mix in a little olive oil, tossing thoroughly. Arrange the spaghetti on individual plates and pour over the mixed vegetables; decorate with olives, add lemon juice, season, and garnish with parsley. (serves 3–4)

Mushroom and cheese pasta

6 oz. mushrooms

1 lb. green lasagne

2 oz. butter

¼ pt. single cream

½ lb. cottage cheese

4 oz. cheddar cheese

parmesan cheese

Sauté the mushrooms in butter; cook lasagne in boiling salted water for 10 minutes, stirring gently with a wooden spoon to ensure that it does not stick together; drain; rinse under cold water to separate. Place a layer of lasagne in greased ovenproof dish, cover with a layer of cream, then one of cheddar cheese, cottage cheese and parmesan, and finally the mushrooms; layer remaining ingredients as described. Add small pieces of butter on top, and bake for 30 minutes in a moderate oven. (serves 8)

Savoury mushroom pancakes

Batter

4 oz. flour

½ pt. milk

1 egg

salt

Filling

8 oz. minced steak

¼ lb. mushrooms

¼ pt. meat stock

1 onion

1 tsp. flour

oregano, oil, seasoning

Fry the onion slices in oil, add meat; season and cook for 5 minutes. Add chopped mushroom and oregano to taste, and cook gently for a further 10 minutes. Add flour, stir in, and add a little stock. Cook for further 5 minutes. Keep hot.

Make pancakes, fill each with approx. 2 tbs. mixture, roll up, and serve at once with accompanying salad or vegetables.

Mixed vegetable casserole

12 oz. mushrooms

4 courgettes sliced

2 onions sliced

½ lb. pasta shapes

2 bananas sliced

16 oz. diced pineapple (or other 'tart' fruit)

1 tbs. cornflour

4 oz. butter

red wine, soy sauce, redcurrant jelly, garlic (optional), seasoning

Sauté the onions and crushed garlic, add courgettes and mushrooms and cook gently until tender. Cook pasta in boiling salted water for 5–10 minutes and drain; add mushrooms, pineapple and banana, stirring well; heat through. Blend corn-flour with red wine, a little water (or juice from canned pineapple), redcurrant jelly and soy sauce. Boil to thicken, toss the vegetables with the sauce, and serve from casserole dish. (serves 6–8)

Devilled mushrooms

12 large mushrooms

1 lb. smaller specimens

1 oz. fat

2 oz. chopped ham

1 small onion finely chopped

curry powder

parsley

breadcrumbs

grated cheese

Chop the smaller mushrooms finely and fry in the fat, with the finely chopped onion; add the ham and approx. 1 teaspoonful Madras curry powder (or to taste) with the parsley. Remove the stalks from the larger mushrooms and place these upside down, with the stalks, in an ovenproof dish. Put some of the mixture on to each cap, cover with grated cheese and breadcrumbs, and pour a little melted butter over each. Bake at Reg. 7 for 10 minutes in a pre–heated oven.

This makes a very attractive dish if each devilled mushroom is placed on a slice of cooked marrow.

Mushroom poultry stuffing

1 lb. mushrooms finely chopped

4 oz. butter and oil mixed

1 small onion chopped

4 oz. fresh breadcrumbs

1 egg

pinch of nutmeg

Melt the butter and oil in a saucepan and gently sauté the mushrooms and onions for 10 minutes; add seasoning. Turn the heat down to low, add the breadcrumbs and stir thoroughly, adding up to $\frac{1}{2}$ cup of water or stock to produce a suitable consistency. Allow the mixture to cool; beat egg and gently fold in to bind the mixture.

The recipe can be varied according to the type of meat you wish to stuff by altering the water/stock ingredient.

Bacon and mushroom rolls

2 oz. mushrooms chopped

2 oz. fresh breadcrumbs

1 small onion finely chopped

8 rashers bacon

mixed herbs

seasoning

1 egg

Mix the fresh breadcrumbs, chopped onion and chopped mushrooms together, adding herbs and seasoning to taste; beat egg and add to bind. Spread the mixture evenly on bacon rashers. Roll and secure with a cocktail stick. Grill for 10 minutes, turning occasionally, or bake in a moderate oven.

This idea is good for parties or as a main dish served with macaroni cheese. (makes 8 rolls)

White mushroom sauce

4 oz. mushrooms finely chopped

1 oz. butter

1 oz. flour

1 pt. milk

Simmer the chopped mushrooms in the milk until tender. Melt the butter in a saucepan, and carefully mix in the flour; add the milk and mushrooms, stirring constantly to avoid lumping, season and cook over a low flame for 20 minutes.

CHAPTER THREE

The Edible Species

The definitive descriptions which follow may seem at first to be full of scientific jargon and littered with long, perhaps unfamiliar words. It might be argued that more everyday language would have sufficed equally, so to vindicate my approach I would offer the following illustration: the expression 'sub–globose' translates far more readably into 'rather rounded'. However, the expression 'sub–globose' means precisely not quite spherical, and indeed 'sub–spherical' is an accepted alternative. On the other hand, what does 'rather rounded' infer? It might mean 'like a cylinder' or 'like a dome'; it might mean 'convex rounded' or 'concave rounded'.

Looking for, and correctly identifying, fungi is not the easiest task; some other aspects—wild flowers or birds for example (I will no doubt incur the displeasure of some experts in those fields)— present on the whole, fewer pitfalls.

Mycological identification often depends on the most incon-spicuous differences of shape, texture or colour being correctly diagnosed. It would be unwise if not altogether foolhardy to approach the subject in any more casual light, particularly when selecting specimens for eating.

Thus, reference books usually adhere to an internationally accepted code of terminology, in which the words used have very precise meanings. Thus the word 'tomentose' means 'thickly downy with soft, matted hairs', whilst 'pilose' means 'covered with longish, easily visible hairs'. It would be inevitable, should this code of terminology not be respected, that each and every writer should develop his own personal terminology, with its accom-panying idiosyncrasies. The result would present the worst kind of confusion for someone trying to carry out correct identification.

A comprehensive glossary of terms can be found on pp. 8–10.

A fundamental stumbling block, when endeavouring to describe living things in a book, is that there is really no such thing as a 'characteristic appearance'. Even a creature such as a mouse, which one might at first imagine to show little possible variation, increases in size and weight with age; its fur elongates and grows coarser; it develops secondary sexual characteristics, and so on.

How then is one accurately to describe the appearance of a fungus which constantly changes, from the first appearance of the young fruiting body, to the time days or weeks later when it finally rots away or shrivels up? Not only does age directly influence appearance, but also climatic conditions; the colour of a fruiting body may be entirely different after a week of drought than that which it assumes during rainy weather. Heavy rainfall may also leach colour from a cap or remove otherwise characteristic velar patches. Decrease in humidity may change a viscid shining cap to a dull, dry one. The amount of humidity in the air can also markedly affect the shape of the cap. One, which is typically planar in damp weather may become infundibuliform after a spell of drought.

There is no obvious solution, and the fungus hunter–at–large needs to be aware that the descriptions in this book cover as many permutations as may reasonably be encountered. It should not be assumed that each description relates to a single characteristic portrait of the fungus.

The accompanying photographs have been taken with a view to showing the specimens in prime mature condition. This, however, will not always help in identification of a newly emergent 'button' or an old, over–ripe cap, nor will it offer 'cast iron' proof of identity when a specimen is viewed in different weather conditions to those prevailing at the time the photograph was taken.

Only first hand experience will really provide all the answers.

Full details of nomenclature are listed for each specimen, for the benefit of the mycologist who wishes to refer back to the authors who originally named the specimen, and a list of the original works is to be found on pp. 235–236.

At the end of the last century, there emerged a trend to 'tag' every plant with a popular name. However, many of these names were short–lived. Nowadays, only certain fungi, having achieved notoriety in some way or other, are generally recognised by common names. I have included these where they are in current usage.

For the purposes of nomenclature, I have rightly or wrongly adhered closely to the check list of Agarics and Boletae, published in 1960, by Dennis, Orton, and Hora in the *Transactions of the British Mycological Society*. Although the nomenclature of fungi, like that of many other facets of biology, is in a constant state of transition, and revision, I think it fair to say that there have been no substantial revisions within the field covered by this book since that list was published. If revisions have occurred, they have been of a localised nature, and I would prefer to reserve judgement on their validity until someone more competent than I publishes a new check list to supercede the 1960 standard.

In any case I would prefer to confront the reader with names that are familiar through establishment in other standard reference books, rather than run the risk of confusion by seeking out and detailing change of specie names, and relocations to different and often strange–sounding genera which may well not be acceptable in any case to the broad mass of mycological thinking.

In the text, the full scientific name of the specimen is given in capitals. Where a synonym has been recently in use, or where there is some dissent about a generic or specie name, the alternative is listed thereafter in brackets, with an asterisked cross–reference.

There follows the abbreviated reference to the author whose nomenclature is currently accepted for the basonym of the specimen. If this reference is the only one listed, then it may be assumed that the author was also responsible for the generic siting of the specimen.

The basis of fungal classification is generally accepted to be the classic work of Elias Fries, compiled from 1867 to 1884 (published posthumously in part), the *Icones Selectae Hymenomycetae*. If the word 'ex' is used, it denotes an author who compiled a description of the fungus prior to an original classification of Fries in 1821, the *Systema Mycologicum*. It can alternatively denote the validation of a name with reference to the original author.

Square brackets enclose a pre–Fries author, when that author used the current specific name attached to a different generic name.

The word 'apud' merely denotes the joining of names of two authors, who arrived at the same classification but who nevertheless worked independently of each other.

The definitive descriptions which follow are partially abbreviated, in accordance with convention. For general ease of following, I have arranged them under headings, in the order by which I think most observers in the field would assess the specimen. Certainly in my own practical experience, I tend to 'run down' a strange specimen by looking at it in the sequence listed.

The descriptions are comprehensive; for example, I have included characteristics of spores, which I know many enthusiasts will welcome. The habitat listed is that in which the specie is most commonly met. However, with the exception of truly obligate relationships, fungi have the odd habit of cropping up in unexpected places, so be prepared for exceptions to the rule. The occurrence is based purely on my own experience and may vary in localised areas throughout the country.

I have been strongly advised to provide an identification key. This, however, is not an easy matter when one is by–passing the broad spectrum of fungi.

CLAVARIA FISTULOSA (CLAVARIADELPHUS) *Fr. *Corner.

Habitat: on dead sticks, or branches of frondose trees, favouring beech; solitary or gregarious, never caespitose.
Dimensions: sporophore 10–30 cm. tall x 2–8 mm. dia.
Sporophore: at first yellow, becoming fulvous, then rufescent and finally more or less date brown; simple, filiform, at first cylindrical, acute at the apex, becoming narrowly sub–clavate, and more obtuse apically, the pedestal longitudinally wrinkled and more or less rooting into the wood. Flesh yellowish, firm and brittle, at first full, becoming hollow. Hymenium spread over upper two–thirds of column. Spores white, narrowly ellipsoidal, smooth 10–18 x 5–9 μ.
Odour: not distinctive.
Occurrence: uncommon. September–January.

RAMARIA FLAVA (Fr.) Quél. Golden clavaria.

Habitat: both frondose and coniferous woods; solitary; on soil.
Dimensions: sporophore 10–20 cm. tall x 6–15 cm. dia.
Sporophore: branches at first primrose yellow, becoming more sulphur yellow, pedestal off–white; all parts bruising brownish, and tending to age brownish. Consisting of many branches arising from a single fleshy basal pedestal, the terminal branchlets extremely numerous, and finely bifurcate. Flesh off–white, soft, slightly elastic. Hymenium spread over branches. Spores yellowish–ochre, ellipsoidal, finely verrucose, 11–18 x 4–6 μ.
Odour: not distinctive.
Occurrence: infrequent. August–October.

CLAVARIADELPHUS PISTILLARIS (CLAVARIA) *(Fr.) Donk. *Fr.

Habitat: frondose woods; typically scattered or gregarious, never caespitose; on soil.
Dimensions: sporophore 7–30 cm. tall x 2–6 cm. dia.
Sporophore: at first pale yellow, becoming deep ochre, and finally rufescent, bruising violaceous brown; simple, at first sub–cylindrical and acute, becoming massively clavate and rounded at the apex like a pestle, the pedestal typically wrinkled longitudinally, otherwise smooth. Flesh white, at first firm and full,

becoming spongy–soft, turning purple where cut. Hymenium spread over apex of pestle. Spores white, pale yellow in the mass, ellipsoidal, smooth 11–16 x 6–10 μ.

Odour: not distinctive. **Taste:** slightly bitter.

Occurrence: occasional. September–December.

RAMARIA BOTRYTIS (CLAVARIA) *(Fr.) Ricken. *Fr. Coral clavaria.

Habitat: frondose and coniferous woods; solitary; on soil.

Dimensions: sporophore 7–15 cm. tall x 6–20 cm. dia.

Sporophore: at first whitish, soon becoming alutaceous, remaining paler in the pedestal, but becoming wine red in the apices. Consisting of many branches arising from a massively broad, irregular basal pedestal; branches divide repeatedly, with the apices terminating in fine bifurcations; the overall effect coral–like. Flesh whitish yellow, wine red in the apices, moist, firm but brittle. Hymenium spread over the branches. Spores pale yellow, ellipsoidal with fine reticulation, 12–20 x 4–6 μ.

Odour: not distinctive. **Taste:** acidic in old specimens.

Occurrence: infrequent. August–October.

MORCHELLA ESCULENTA (L.) Pers. Morel.

Habitat: light frondose woods, in grassy clearings, shady gardens, hedgerows, favouring rich soil; solitary; on soil.

Dimensions: cap 4–10 cm. tall x 3–5 cm. dia.; stipe 4–8 cm. tall x 2–3 cm. dia.

Cap: fulvous; obtusely ovoid or rounded, margin connate with stipe, the surface folded into irregular cavities bearing the hymenial surface, and bounded by acute sterile ridges. Flesh pale yellowish, fragile. Spores hyaline, white in the mass, ellipsoidal, smooth, 18–24 x 10–12 μ.

Stipe: pallid yellowish, slightly flexuose, may be plicate above, otherwise more or less smooth and minutely squamulose to velvety, becoming brownish at the base in older specimens. Flesh pale yellowish, thin, fragile, hollow.

Odour: not distinctive.

Occurrence: occasional. March–May.

Morels are all vernal fungi, appearing in the spring, for which reason many enthusiasts probably have never seen one.

They are considered to be great delicacies, but I must stress that they all contain minute quantities of helvellic acid, and therefore must be thoroughly cooked to remove this poisonous principle. Perhaps the greatest risk is in the danger of confusing them with *Gyromitra esculenta,* also vernal, but dangerously poisonous in some instances. The obvious difference between the two types is that the cap of *Gyromitra* develops *convex bulges,* whereas the cap of a morel is pitted with concavities.

In Italy, morels are cooked by first dressing them with fresh mixed herbs and seasoning, coat liberally with oil and stew until the juice runs out: thicken mixture with a little flour; serve with breadcrumbs and a garnish of lemon.

MORCHELLA CONICA Pers. Morel.

Habitat: light mixed woods, and coniferous woods, in grassy clearings, shady gardens etc favouring rich soil; solitary; on soil.

Dimensions: cap 2–6 cm. tall x 1.5–3.0 cm. dia.; stipe 2–4 cm. tall x 2.0–2.5 cm. dia.

Cap: dark olive brown, conical, margin connate with stipe, surface folded into regular rectangular cavities, bearing the hymenial surface, and bounded by sterile, longitudinal principal ridges, connected by smaller, narrower cross ridges. Flesh yellowish olive, fragile, thin. Spores hyaline, white in the mass, ellipsoidal, smooth, 18–20 x 12–15 μ.

Stipe: off–white to pale yellowish brown; apex of almost equal breadth with cap, slightly attenuated downwards; slightly plicate, farinose. Flesh yellowish, very fragile, thin, hollow.

Odour: not distinctive.

Occurrence: occasional. April–May.

MORCHELLA SEMI–LIBERA DC Morel.

Habitat: light mixed woods, copses, shady gardens etc favouring damp rich soil; solitary; on soil.

Dimensions: cap 2–6 cm. tall x 2–4 cm. dia.; stipe 4–9 cm. tall x 2–3 cm. dia.

Cap: olive brown; quite small relative to stipe length; conical to briefly campanulate, margin not connate with stipe; surface folded into shallow depressions, bearing the hymenial surface, bounded by sterile, acute longitudinal principal ridges, connected by smaller cross ridges. Flesh off–white, thin, fragile. Spores

hyaline, white in the mass, ellipsoidal, smooth, 22–25 x 12–14 μ.
Stipe: off–white at first, becoming slightly brownish yellow; faintly scrobiculate, minutely farinose; at least twice cap height. Flesh off–white, thin, fragile, hollow.
Odour: not distinctive.
Occurrence: occasional. March–May.

MORCHELLA VULGARIS (Pers.) Boud. Morel.

Habitat: light mixed woods, grassy places, shady gardens etc favouring damp, rich soil; solitary; on soil.
Dimensions: cap 3–6 cm. tall x 2–4 cm. dia.; stipe 2–5 cm. tall x 1.5–2.5 cm. dia.
Cap: dark olive brown or greyish brown; ovoid, margin connate with stipe; surface folded into very irregular cavities bearing the hymenial surface, and bounded by blunt sterile ridges. Flesh yellowish, thin, fragile. Spores hyaline, white in the mass, ellipsoidal, smooth 18–22 x 10–12 μ.
Stipe: yellowish cream, smooth or faintly scrobiculate, may be minutely farinose. Flesh yellowish, thin, fragile, hollow.
Odour: not distinctive.
Occurrence: occasional. March–May.

SPARASSIS CRISPA (Wulf.) Fr. Cauliflower fungus.

Habitat: bases of old, rotting conifer stumps, typically pine or spruce; may be actually inside a hollow stump; on wood.
Dimensions: very variable 10–20 cm. tall x 15–30 cm. dia.; larger specimens have been recorded.
Sporophore: at first impression looking like a loose cauliflower; at first creamy white, becoming more yellowish, and finally tan colour from spore dust; approximately spherical consisting of a dark brown or blackish pedestal, rooting into the wood, expanding into many fleshy branchlets; hymenium spread on either side of branchlets which are wavy to lobate with irregularly dentate margins. Flesh white elastic but brittle, sub–fibrillar. Spores pale yellowish cream, tan colour in the mass, briefly ellipsoidal, smooth 6–7 x 4–5 μ.
Odour: not distinctive. **Taste:** faintly nutty.
Occurrence: at one time quite frequent, but becoming rather uncommon with increase in reclamation of old timber land. August–October.

41

Sparassis crispa (young sporop

Sparassis is one of those extraordinary, once–seen–never–forgotten type fungi. It is quite impossible to confuse it with anything else and affords a rewarding sight, when one peers into an old pine stump and is confronted with this large creamy, cauliflower object nestling there.

Regrettably, with the present day premium placed on good forestry land, there seems to be less and less of the sort of good old–fashioned mixed wood, where trees are allowed to decay and fall of their own accord. So potential growing places for *Sparassis* are becoming less easy to find.

If you are lucky enough to find one of these growths, it must be young to be of value for cooking. Once the fruiting body has turned yellow, it is probably too tough and indigestible, so do not bother about anything that is not really fresh–looking and the palest cream in colour.

The simplest way to cook *Sparassis* is by sauteing. To pre–pare, cut off the stalk and discard, then slice the 'cauliflower' into convenient portions and wash thoroughly before cooking. Sauté gently for a full 20 minutes, until very tender. As the taste is mild with a slightly nutty overtone, add a sprinkling of herbs, along with salt and pepper, to enhance the flavour.

An alternative method of cooking is to place the pieces in a casserole with butter, milk and plenty of seasoning. Again, allow the fungus adequate time to cook gently.

Sparassis can readily be dried and stored. It is worth dissect–ing into small pieces first, otherwise the centre may start to decay before properly dry.

If one ever comes across one of these odd fungi, it is well worth the effort of taking home and preparing. It is in great demand on the Continent, where a preferred way to cook it is by cutting into slices and coating with whisked egg. Larger specimens are kept fresh by putting the base in a bowl of water in a cool, dark place, and cutting off pieces as required. Apparently this practice keeps the fungus fresh and wholesome for some time and saves using it all at once.

TUBER AESTIVUM Vitt. Truffle.

Habitat: subterranean, on calcareous soils, favouring beech.
Dimensions: sporophore 2–8 cm. dia.
Sporophore: dark brown, to black, with purplish tinge; tuberous, irregular globose; covered with regular pentagonal scabs. Fertile interior greyish cream colour, typically with purplish tinge, criss–crossed with pallid irregular reticulations. Spores hyaline, white in the mass, reticulate, 20–40 x 15–30 μ.
Odour: not distinctive. **Taste:** nutty.
Occurrence: uncertain, owing to difficulty in locating.

44   *Tuber aest*

Truffles have achieved enormous popularity in the past and are extensively referred to in Roman literature. The Romans used pigs to locate truffles. The pigs seem to have a particularly sensitive nose for them and root them out from under leaves. In France poodle dogs are trained to carry out the same function, and in Germany there is a similar 'trufflehund'.

The Continental variety, *T. melanosporum,* is more greatly esteemed than the British species. Although truffle hunting has now died out in the British Isles at one time it had achieved great popularity.

The truffle counties were considered to be Dorset, Hamp—shire, Sussex, and Kent, through which the chalk downlands run, with their attendant beech woods. However, today truffling has become a lost art, and unless you are prepared to spend a day on your hands and knees, sifting through beech leaves and litter, you stand little chance of taking any home for supper.

The Romans had special recipes for cooking truffles. They were sliced, boiled, seasoned, transfixed with twigs, and partly roasted. Next they were popped into a cooking pot with oil, liquamen, caroenum, pepper and honey, boiled again, and finally dished up to the by then ravening patricians.

An interesting alternative was to bag the truffles in the omentum of a pig, and then to roast the whole together as a sort of imperial haggis!

A Victorian recipe more simply advocates boiling, or roasting in hot ashes.

My own initiation into truffle hunting was by John Bassindale, head gardener of a fine old manor house in the Sussex chalk downs. Contrary to most literature on the subject, truffles are not so much limited to beech woods as to chalk soils, in fact, the specimens I was shown were growing under an Ilex, or 'evergreen oak'. Here the top soil was quite firm, with a scanty covering of leaves. The truffles lay with approximately the top quarter of the tuber above ground, and the rest buried. It is not too difficult to pick out the very characteristic black pentagonal scales against the more even textured top soil, once the eye is accustomed to the shape.

I was surprised that, again contrary to popular belief, the tubers were found not in early autumn but in late April. Inspection revealed them to be fresh and in a mid—term stage of development. I feel, therefore, that truffles are probably to be found during most of the year, in selected localities.

There are probably many more truffles around than one might imagine, but a lot of patience and a certain amount of local knowledge may well be needed before one has much chance of finding any. At any rate, they seem to appear with regularity in the same places year after year.

CANTHARELLUS CIBARIUS Fr. Chantarelle.

Habitat: mixed woods; solitary or scattered; on soil.
Dimensions: cap very variable, up to 6 cm. dia.; stipe 1–4 cm. tall x 1.5–2.5 cm. dia.
Cap: egg yellow to apricot; at first sub–convex, and slightly umbilicate, soon becoming strongly infundibuliform, with irregular, undulating, sub–lobate margin; cuticle dull, glabrous. Flesh egg yellow, with rather rubbery texture.
Gills: no true gills, but hymenium spread over irregular folds, concolorous with cap, forming blunt, shallow, deeply decurrent forked ridges. Spores hyaline, white when viewed singly, pale yellow in the mass, ellipsoidal, smooth 8–10 cm. x 5–6 μ.
Stipe: concolorous with cap; at first smooth, becoming reticulate in older specimens; slightly attenuated downwards. Flesh egg yellow, firm.
Odour: fruity. **Taste:** peppery.
Occurrence: common, but becoming less frequent. August–November.

The Victorians make little mention of this excellent fungus, though it has long been popular in France, where it is known also as 'la girolle', and in Italy. In country districts it is traditionally dried or pickled for use in the winter. Nowadays, however, the woods anywhere near urban centres in Europe have been disastrously overpicked, and the fungus is becoming something of a rarity.

Its chief claim to fame in England seems to be that it was once served up on state occasions at the Freemasons Tavern in London. Collected around Chelmsford, it was much sought after as a novelty and fetched high prices in restaurants.

The main drawback is that the fungus is rather tough, though of excellent, slightly peppery, flavour. One way of making it more tender is to soak it overnight in milk. In any event it requires long and careful stewing. I suggest slicing the fungi lengthways into quarters and then simmering for a good hour in milk and butter, with only a dash of seasoning. Make a white sauce with the juice and pour over the cooked slices.

Although the preparation is somewhat involved, it is well worth the effort. Difficulty, however, may be experienced in collecting enough specimens to make a worthwhile meal

Cantharellus cibarius

CANTHARELLUS CINEREUS (Fr.) Pat.

Habitat: frondose woods; solitary, gregarious, or caespitose; on soil, but generally in proximity of tree roots.

Dimensions: cap 2–4 cm. dia.; stipe 3–6 cm. tall x 0.5–1.0 cm. dia.

Cap: inside (upper) surface brownish grey, generally paler in dry weather; deeply infundibuliform and hollow, tubular to base, margin irregular; cuticle scurfy–squamulose towards centre, more glabrous at margin. Flesh grey, cartilaginous, brittle, thin.

Gills: no true gills, but hymenium spread over wrinkles, distant, more or less dichotomous, with some anastomosing upwards, and transverse reticulations. Hymenial surface, paler more ash grey than upper surface, becoming whitish grey as spores ripen and dust over it. Spores hyaline, white in the mass, obtuse, finely granular, 7–8 x 5–6 μ.

Odour: fruity.

Occurrence: not common. September–October.

Both this fungus and the related *C. infundibuliformis* are not unlike the chantarelle in texture; both are somewhat aromatic and, although the latter is a little bitter in the raw state, make excellent eating.

Prepare them by a good overnight soaking, and cook in the same way as for the chantarelle.

CANTHARELLUS INFUNDIBULIFORMIS Fr.

Habitat: frondose and coniferous woods, favouring acid soils; gregarious but not caespitose; on soil.

Dimensions: cap 2–5 cm. dia.; stipe 2–7 cm. tall x 1.0–1.5 cm. dia.

Cap: inside (upper) surface mid–brown to dark brown or blackish, generally paler in dry weather; deeply infundibuliform, but not hollow to base, margin wavy but fairly regular; cuticle minutely squamulose. Flesh pallid, tough, cartilaginous, thin.

Gills: no true gills, but hymenium spread over branched, blunt, irregular wrinkles. Hymenial surface at first pale yellow, becoming greyish white. Spores hyaline, white in the mass, obtuse, finely granular, 8–10 x 6–8 μ.

Odour: faintly aromatic.

Occurrence: common. August–December.

Cantharellus infundibuliformis

CRATERELLUS CORNUCOPIOIDES ([L.] Fr.) Pers. Horn of plenty.

Habitat: frondose woods, favouring beech; typically grega–
rious; on soil.
Dimensions: cap 5–12 cm. dia.; stipe 3–8 cm. tall x 1–2 cm. dia.
Cap: inside (upper) surface dark brownish, smokey grey,
generally paler in dry weather; at once deeply infundibuliform and
hollow, tubular to the base, margin undulate or lobate, crinkled,
partly involute and partly revolute; cuticle squamulose. Flesh
grey, cartilaginous, brittle.
Gills: no true gills, but hymenium spread over branching and
anastomosing wrinkles on outside (lower) surface. Hymenial
surface paler than upper surface, becoming more ash grey as spores
ripen and dust over it. Spores hyaline, ovate, smooth 12–14 x
7–8 μ.
Odour: not distinctive.
Occurrence: fairly common. August–November.

The horn of plenty is ideal for pickling or drying and
powdering. When wholly dried out it is completely black and very
fragile.
A traditional Neapolitan method of preparing the fungus is
to cut the fruiting bodies into thin slices and then boil once or
twice in milk. The cooked pieces are then beaten on a board and
fried in oil.
In Scandinavia, it is prepared by putting in a casserole with
a liberal dousing of butter and baking gently.

GRIFOLIA FRONDOSA (Dicks) Gray.

Habitat: on bases and rotten stumps of frondose trees,
favouring oak, but also recorded on hornbeam and apple;
caespitose fused and densely imbricate.
Dimensions: sporophore mass 15–30 cm. dia.; individual caps
4–8 cm. dia.
Fungus consisting of up to one hundred fairly small, greyish
brown caps, arising from bulbous trunk, made up of entirely
connate stipes, each of which divides out to serve an individual
cap.
Cap: greyish brown or occasionally brownish yellow;
spathulate, widely ligulate, or wedge shaped, with rounded
margin; laterally sessile; cuticle radially plicate and fibrillose,

Craterellus cornucopioides

dull. Flesh white, medium, soft, juicy.

Pores: off–white, irregular to polygonal. Tubes deeply decurrent, concolorous with pores, very short. Spores hyaline, white in the mass, elongate, sub–cylindrical, smooth, 7–10 x 2.5–4.0 μ.

Stipe: white, very short arising from common trunk, smooth. Flesh white, sub–fibrillar, juicy.

Odour: at first reminiscent of aniseed (Pilât), later becoming rancid.

Occurrence: uncommon. September–November.

Although one is unlikely to come across this splendid fungus often, on the odd occasion when it does come to hand, it will result in a meal of its own, since the fruiting body can weigh as much as 3 kilos.

As is to be expected with this sort of fungus, all but the youngest caps tend to be somewhat tough; it therefore requires long and careful cooking. However, once this problem is over–come, you have a delicious, gently aromatic dish to tuck into. The fungus is impossible to confuse with any other species and is quite a sight, almost awe–inspiring when you suddenly catch sight of it through the trees, sprouting like some giant science–fiction growth.

FISTULINA HEPATICA (Huds.) Fr. Poor man's beefsteak; Oak tongue.

Habitat: parasitic on frondose trees, favouring oak, sweet chestnut, and willow. The mycelium stains the wood a rich brown, which may be favoured in cut oak timber. Solitary or less frequently caespitose, occasionally imbricate.

Dimensions: 10–25 cm. dia.; (2–5 cm. thick).

Sporophore: typically orange or pinkish red when young, blood red at maturity and later dull, dark brown; hoof shaped, reniform or semi–circular, laterally sessile or less commonly with short lateral stipe; thick, spongy and gelatinous, flesh oozing reddish juice like blood, particularly in wet weather. Upper cuticle verrucose–papillate; lower surface bearing hymenium at first creamy white, rufescent where bruised, later wholly rufous. Tubes minute, mutually free, opening by circular pores. Flesh blood red, with radiating paler zones, thick and juicy. Spores flesh coloured, sub–hyaline and ovate 4–5 x 3–4 μ.

Odour: not distinctive. **Taste:** acidic.

Occurrence: occasional. August–November.

53   *Fistulina hepatica*

Although the flesh looks remarkably like raw meat and the culinary virtue has at times been described in glowing terms— Smith places it as 'a treat for an epicure', and Badham maintains 'it is scarcely to be distinguished from broiled meat'—the beefsteak fungus is hardly exciting, certainly not to my palate. The acidic flavour is largely muted when the specimen is well cooked, and indeed some may approve of the piquant flavour, but the dish needs to be well seasoned. An alternative use is to stew the specimens well, discard the flesh, and use the juice as stock.

Some recommend the inclusion of raw slices in salad to add a refreshing tartness. However, all in all, I think the experimenter will be disappointed, and the 'poor man's beefsteak' is certainly an unappetising substitute for the real thing.

HYDNUM REPANDUM L. ex Fr. Hedgehog fungus.

Habitat: frondose woods, favouring beech; typically gregari–ous, and often in rings; on soil.

Dimensions: cap 3–12 cm. dia.; stipe 3–7 cm. tall x 0.5–2.0 cm dia.

Cap: cream colour, occasionally varying towards pinkish or yellowish tinge; at first convex, soon becoming irregularly plane, lobate, with slightly involute margin; cuticle dull, pruinose, typically glabrous but may be slightly tomentose, surface often irregularly cracked giving appearance not unlike that of a freshly baked scone. Flesh off–white, thick and firm.

Gills: replaced by spines, concolorous with cap; to a variable extent decurrent, conical when young, later becoming flattened in cross section. Spores white, sub–hyaline, sub–globose, faintly reticulate, 7.0 x 6.0 μ.

Stipe: off–white to pale cream, typically slightly excentric, short and stout, or pruinose. Flesh off–white, thick, firm.

Odour: not distinctive. **Taste:** acrid.

Occurrence: common locally. August–November.

People may well be put off by the bitter taste of this fungus, which will persist if the specimens are cooked in the more usual ways. However, it is quite easy to remove the bitterness, after which the fungus is quite tasty, though its texture is rather granular and some find it indigestible.

The specimens should be cleaned, cut in smallish pieces and then boiled for five minutes in plain water. By draining this off and discarding, the unpleasant taste is effectively removed.

Hydnum repandum

Hydnum repandum (showing colour variat

There is no indication at present that the bitter constituent is in any way poisonous, and whichever way the fungus is cooked it is harmless, even though it may be unpalatable before carrying out the routine described above.

I would venture the following suggestion for cooking the debittered fungus:

1 lb. fungus

1 oz. butter

$\frac{1}{2}$ pt. single cream

$\frac{1}{4}$ pt. milk

2 oz. breadcrumbs

seasoning and fresh parsley

Having removed the bitterness as described, place the pieces in a casserole and stir in the milk and cream. Season well and sprinkle the breadcrumbs over the top, adding small pats of butter. Bake for 20 minutes at 350°F without covering the casserole, and garnish with parsley before serving. Serve with croutons. (serves 3–4)

The rules to follow generally with *Hydnum* are thorough cooking and the use of plenty of fluid, because they are other-wise rather deficient in moisture.

In Italy they are frequently sold with chantarelles and are known as 'steccherinos' or little hedgehogs. I have read some-where that their taste is vaguely reminiscent of oysters—perhaps they have aphrodisiac qualities too!

HYDNUM RUFESCENS Fr.

Habitat: both frondose and coniferous woods; typically gregarious; on soil.

Dimensions: cap 3–8 cm. dia.; stipe 3–5 cm. tall x 1.0–2.0 cm. dia.

Cap: cream colour with reddish brown patches, or wholly reddish brown; at first convex soon becoming irregularly plane, lobate with slightly incurved margin. Cuticle dull, pruinose, typically glabrous but may be slightly tomentose; surface often irregularly cracked giving appearance not unlike that of freshly baked loaf. Flesh off–white, thick and firm.

Gills: replaced by spines, concolorous with cap; to a variable extent only slightly decurrent, conical when young later becoming flattened in cross section. Spores white, sub–hyaline, sub–globose, 7–8 x 6–7 μ.

Stipe: concolorous with cap cuticle but paler, short and stout, smooth, pruinose. Flesh off–white, firm.

Odour: not distinctive. **Taste:** acidic.

Occurrence: common locally. August–November.

AGARICUS ARVENSIS (Schaeff. ex Secr.) Lange. Horse mushroom.

Habitat: typically in pastures, less common at edges of coniferous woods, and in firebreaks of plantations; solitary or in small groups; on soil.

Dimensions: cap 5–12 cm. dia.; stipe 6–14 cm. tall x 1.5–2.5 cm. dia.

Cap: white at first, yellowing in older specimens, turning chrome yellow on bruising; at first spherical or slightly conical, becoming convex, and finally expanded–convex or plano–expanded; cuticle smooth, glabrous, silky shining in dry weather. Flesh white, turning chrome yellow where cut; firm and moderately thick.

Gills: at first pallid with greyish tinge, finally chocolate brown with purple tinge, never pink; free, narrow. Spores chocolate brown with purple tinge, ovoid, smooth, 8–10 x 4.5–5.5 μ. (slightly larger than in *A. silvicola*).

Stipe: white at first, but yellowing in older specimens, and chrome yellow where cut or bruised; thickish, attenuated upwards, without basal bulb (contrast with *A. silvicola*); annulus white, lax, membraneous with double margin, the lower margin frilled, but narrower than that of *A. silvicola*. Flesh white, chrome yellow where cut.

Odour: distinctly of aniseed.

Occurrence: occasional, but with higher localised frequency. August–October.

The size and shape of this mushroom make it eminently suitable for stuffing with either a whole tomato or onion, or filling with sage and onion, or minced steak. What about slices of marrow, and topping with a cheese sauce?

All the ensuing members of the *Agaricus* family can be cooked in much the same ways as the commercial mushroom. There are, however, two points to bear in mind.

When collecting *Agaricus* spp. it is important to note that in many of them the gills do not pass through a flesh pink stage but pass from a rather pallid colour, straight to shades of brown, finishing up with the characteristic dark chocolate of the mature spores.

Most of the wild *Agaricus* spp. smell reminiscent of aniseed, or fennel. Most people find this pleasant, but if you don't like the particular .odour, then mix the mushrooms with other prominent flavours.

AGARICUS AUGUSTUS Fr. Large wood mushroom.

Habitat: mixed woods, favouring spruce; solitary, or in small groups; on soil.

Dimensions: cap 12–20 cm. dia.; stipe 15–25 cm. tall x 2.5–3.0 cm. dia.

Cap: pale date brown or hazel at first, cuticle breaking up as the cap expands into minute, adpressed, fibrillose squamules, arranged concentrically in rows, on more golden yellow back– ground, except at disc which is more or less smooth or slightly cracked, squamules less crowded towards cap margin; at first sub–spherical becoming convex–expanded and finally bluntly conical or wholly plano–expanded. Flesh white, becoming yellowish with age, thick, soft, turning yellowish where cut.

Gills: at first pallid, finally chocolate brown, never pink; free, crowded, narrow. Spores chocolate brown with purple tinge, ovate, smooth, 7–10 x 5–6 μ.

Stipe: at first off–white, and squamulose below annulus, becoming more or less glabrous as the cap expands, finally dirty yellowish and bruising yellow; annulus white, large, lax, membraneous; base of stipe may be slightly clavate but not bulbous. Flesh white, thick, and soft, brownish at base of stipe.

Odour: distinctly of aniseed.

Occurrence: occasional. August–October.

AGARICUS LANGEI Fr. Red staining mushroom.

Habitat: frondose woods and grassy places; solitary or in small groups; on soil.

Dimensions: cap 7–10 cm. dia.; stipe 4–8 cm. tall x 1.5–2.5 cm. dia.

Cap: cinnamon brown, closely adpressed with darker, rusty brown, fibrillose scales; at first hemispherical and tending to remain convex. Flesh white but crimson where cut, fairly thin.

Gills: at first pink, becoming brown and finally dark chocolate; free and rather brittle. Spores chocolate, ovate, smooth 7–8 x 4–5 μ.

Stipe: off–white; annulus typically absent; stout but without bulbous base. Flesh at first white, soon discolouring dull brown; crimson where cut or bruised; stuffed.

Odour: not distinctive.

Occurrence: occasional. September–November.

Instantly recognisable by its peculiar characteristic of bruising bright red, this fungus has all the wholesome qualities of a good wild mushroom. Although it is by no means common, one can occasionally find a small group of them, which are well worth collecting for the table.

AGARICUS BISPORUS (var. *albida*). (Large.) Pilât.
Cultivated mushroom.

Habitat: not generally found in the wild, but occasionally appearing as an escape from mushroom compost.

Dimensions: cap 5–10 cm. dia.; stipe 3–6 cm. tall x 2.0–3.5 cm. dia.

Cap: at first pure white, later becoming more off–white or slightly brownish at disc; at first hemispherical but flattened at the disc, later plane with long involute margin, and finally wholly plane to slightly depressed, cap margin always projecting below the gills; cuticle silky–fibrillose, floccose at the margin with volval remains; thickly fleshy, flesh white.

Gills: pale salmon pink when young, becoming darker and finally chocolate brown in old specimens, free, fairly broad. Spores deep purple brown, broadly ellipsoidal, smooth 7–8 x 5–6 μ. Basidium bears 2 spores only.

Stipe: white, stout and short, slightly attenuated downwards; floccose to silky below annulus, slightly sulcate above; annulus membraneous lax, and two–layered with margin typically frayed; flesh white, faintly rufescent when cut.

Odour: distinctive.

The modern commercial variety of mushroom is not the 'field mushroom', *Agaricus campestris,* but the species described above, so named because each basidium bears only two basidio–

61

Agaricus augustus

Agaricus

spores, as opposed to the more typical number of four.

It can occasionally be found in the wild, on roadsides and manure heaps but is probably an 'escape' from commercial compost which has been improperly sterilised after use.

Today, mushroom growing is a highly scientific operation, but its origins go back as far as the end of the 17th century. Someone, whose name has not survived on record, reportedly found a way of innoculating wild mushroom spawn into horse manure, so that mushrooms grew in it. 'Spawn' by the way, is not, as the word probably sounds, 'spores', but originally was part of the fungus mycelium lifted from the field and is now used to describe a carefully prepared extract of the tissues of the actual sporophore.

In 1707, a method of growing mushrooms on horse manure was properly written up by de Tournefort in Paris, and his techniques were religiously followed until the beginning of the 20th century.

Although for a brief period during the latter part of the 19th century British growers held the limelight in mushroom growing and exported spawn all over the world, the French pioneered commercial mushroom growing in underground quarries around Paris. Horse manure was stacked in great heaps and allowed to heat up naturally by its own fermentation, and the resulting compost was spread out in long ridges. Mushroom spawn was collected on an extremely haphazard basis, practically anywhere that horses frequented, like canal tow paths, and after incubation in the compost, frequently produced more toadstools than edible fungi.

The main difficulty was that no one had as yet evolved a reliable technique for isolating pure mushroom spawn. In 1894 the French workers, Constantin and Matruchot, managed to isolate viable spawn, although for some reason their method was patented but never put to commercial use.

The interest had by then switched to America where, eleven years later, Duggar perfected the method of extracting pure spawn from mushroom tissues that is used today.

For many years, the traditional way of growing mushrooms was underground. Although as early as 1754 someone in Sweden advocated the use of greenhouses for the purpose, it was only recently that standard growing houses were properly evolved with independently controlled conditions of temperature, aeration, and humidity.

Today there are many and varied recipes for making mush-room compost, but certain underlying principles are to be found in all of them.

The basis of the compost on which the mushrooms are grown is usually horse manure mixed with horses' bedding straw, now obtained from riding establishments, stud farms, and racing stables.

The mixture is first composted in long stacks, about six feet

Agaricus bisporus (young sporoph

65   *Agaricus bisporus* (mature sporophores)

wide and six feet high, where it is allowed to heat up by the action of resident bacteria and fungi in much the same way as a compost heap in the garden. This fermentation produces temperatures as high as 170–180°F. The stacks are turned mechanically at intervals, over a period of twelve days, to keep them well aerated and to allow the microflora to work.

The compost is then ready for pasteurization. It is taken into the growing sheds and spread in trays to a depth of 8–12″ and subjected to various processes, during which it is maintained at 140°F. It is then allowed to cool. When it reaches 75–80°F the spawn is planted.

The incubation period, at temperatures between 72–75°F, is ten to twelve days, after which the fungal mycelium has completely invaded the compost. A layer of sterile 'soil' made from a mixture of peat and chalk is spread evenly over the beds to a depth of 2″, known as 'casing', and the beds are then left for the sporo–phores to develop.

The vigorous growth of the mycelium keeps the temperature in the bed between 72–85°F, and three weeks after 'casing' the first crop is ready for picking. After the first crop or 'flush', the beds are heavily watered to encouraged the next 'flush', which is ready for picking about a week later. Subsequent 'flushes' become more and more unproductive, and after the bed has been cropped about five times, it is usually sterilised out, or 'cooked', by heating the growing house to a temperature of 170°F. Thus the carry–over of any disease to the next crop is effectively prevented.

By the end of its life in the mushroom shed, each ton of compost will probably have produced up to 400 lb. of mushrooms for despatch to markets, shops and canneries.†

AGARICUS SILVICOLA (Vitt.) Peck. Common wood mushroom.

Habitat: typically under conifers, less frequent in frondose woods; solitary, or in small groups; on soil.

Dimensions: cap 6–10 cm. dia.; stipe 7–12 cm. tall x 1.5–2.5 cm. dia.

Cap: white at first, yellowing in older specimens, turning chrome yellow on bruising; at first spherical or slightly conical, becoming convex, and finally expanded–convex or plano–expanded; cuticle smooth, glabrous, silky shining in dry weather. Flesh white, turning chrome yellow where cut; firm and moderately thick.

---

†(I am indebted to Messrs W. Darlington and Sons Ltd, of Rustington, Sussex, whose kind assistance has facilitated the detailing of this process.)

Agaricus silvicola

Gills: at first pallid with greyish tinge, finally chocolate brown with purple tinge, never pink; free, narrow. Spores chocolate brown with purple tinge, ovate, smooth, 5.5–6.5 x 3.5–4.0 μ. (slightly smaller than in *A. arvensis*).

Stipe: white at first, but yellowing in older specimens, and chrome yellow where cut or bruised; thickish, attenuated upwards, with distinctive, flat, truncated basal bulb (contrast with *A. arvensis*). Annulus white, lax, membraneous with double margin, the lower margin distinctly frilled, wider than that of *A. arvensis*. Flesh white, chrome yellow where cut.

Odour: distinctly of aniseed.

Occurrence: fairly common. August–October.

AGARICUS SYLVATICUS Schaeff. ex Secr. Wood mushroom.

Habitat: under coniferous and frondose trees but favouring spruce; more prevalent in limestone regions; gregarious; on soil.

Dimensions: cap 5–8 cm. dia.; stipe 7–12 cm. tall x 1.5–2.5 cm. dia.

Cap: cinnamon brown, closely adpressed with darker, rusty brown, short, fibrillose scales. At first convex, becoming plano–expanded. Flesh white, but slightly rufescent where cut, thin, compared with other *Agaricus* spp.; thick.

Gills: at first pale brownish pink, becoming brown and finally dark chocolate; free and rather brittle. Spores chocolate, ovate smooth 5–6 x 3–4 μ.

Stipe: off–white; prominent annulus standing high up on stipe, two–layered at margin and at first standing off, later more lax, base slightly bulbous, attenuating slightly upwards. Flesh at first white later becoming dull brown; at first stuffed, becoming hollow; thick.

Odour: wood mixed with snuffed candle (Schaeffer).

Occurrence: localised. September–November.

An excellent edible specimen, with all the qualities of a good tasty wild mushroom, and hardly to be confused with anything suspect, but alas, in my own experience, by no means common.

Any of the suggested methods for cooking bought mushrooms to be found in recipe books are applicable here.

Agaricus sylvaticus

AMANITA FULVA [Schaeff.] Secr. Tawny grisette.

Habitat: frondose woods generally, but favouring more acid soils, particularly under birch.
Dimensions: cap 4–10 cm. dia.; stipe 8–12 cm. tall x 0.8–1.3 cm. dia.
Cap: orange brown, becoming slightly more date brown towards disc; at first conical–campanulate, becoming expanded and slightly umbonate; cuticle glabrous, smooth, striate and sulcate or pectinate at margin. Flesh pallid, fragile, thin.
Gills: off–white to cream, free, crowded and soft. Spores hyaline, white in the mass, globose, smooth, 8–10 μ.
Stipe: whitish flesh colour, smooth, slender and attenuated upwards; no annulus present, but the base of the stipe sheathed with whitish, lobately torn volva. At first loosely stuffed, becoming hollow.
Odour: not distinctive.
Occurrence: fairly common. July–November.

At one time, both this fungus and its close relative, the grisette *(A. vaginata),* were separately classified as *Amanitopsis,* on account of their lack of an annulus, but have now been relocated.
However, in spite of affinities with more sinister specimens, both the grisette and the tawny grisette are sufficiently distinctive to render identification fairly easy.
A. vaginata is probably uncommon in most areas of the British Isles and tends more towards open heath land. It is similar to *A. fulva* in all respects except cap colour, which is pale grey, with a suspicion of tan towards the centre.
In both forms, the fruiting body first makes its appearance as an oval egg–like structure, completely surrounded by the volva and partly sunk into the ground. However, when mature, the delicate appearance of the cap and the long, slender stipe, without annulus, are very distinctive. Anyone who has once seen a grisette is most unlikely to confuse it with any of the dangerous Amanitas. The only form with remotely similar colour is *A. muscaria,* but the whole structure of the sporophore is altogether more massive, and there is no volval bag.
However, I cannot advocate the selection of any *Amanita* fungi for eating without the certainty of its identification, to be had by going out collecting with an expert.
The Victorians seem to have by–passed grisettes as objects of culinary virtue, perhaps on account of their fragile appearance, and I can find no reference to their use on the Continent.
However, the flavour is pleasantly strong, and the texture,

Amanita fulva

as one might guess from the appearance of the fungus, is delicate. Their occurrence is sufficiently prolific in most years to make collection of a reasonable number practicable, and the specimens can be either mixed with other forms, or, I would suggest, served in a white sauce, with lemon.

Certainly a species worth trying if you are sure of identity and come across a reasonable quantity. I always find them to be one of the prettiest of autumn fungi.

AMANITA RUBESCENS ([Pers.] Fr.) Gray. The blusher.

Habitat: frondose and coniferous woods; solitary; on soil.

Dimensions: cap 6–15 cm. dia.; stipe 6–16 cm. tall x 2.0–3.5 cm. dia.

Cap: dull reddish brown, covered with small verrucose remnants of veil, variable in colour from pale clay to reddish, never truly white; at first spherical, and adpressed to stipe, becoming convex, and finally plano–expanded; cuticle slightly furrowed in older specimens, at the margin, but not sulcate. Flesh white, quickly rufescent where cut or damaged (e.g. by insect bites), rather thin at margin, otherwise thick.

Gills: white, typically with rufescent spots in older specimens, free, broad, crowded, rather soft. Spores hyaline, white in the mass, ellipsoidal, smooth 8–10 x 6–7 μ.

Stipe: pale clay colour, usually reddish at the base; thick and slightly attenuated upwards; annulus large, pendant, sulcate above, white or pale flesh colour, typically with rufescent edge; base of stipe only slightly bulbous, with several rows of small, verrucose volval remnants. Flesh white, but quickly rufescent where cut, at first full, becoming more spongy stuffed, and frequently hollow in old specimens,

Odour: not distinctive. **Taste:** at first pleasantly sweet, then astringent on the throat.

Occurrence: frequent. August–November.

The most characteristic aspect of this fungus is its habit of quickly acquiring a red 'blush' where the flesh is damaged. This accounts for its common name and makes it easily recognisable.

I must at once stress that this is not a specimen for the beginner to seek out, because it is a member of the *Amanita* group, which contains a number of deadly species that are closely related to the fungus described here. It is quite conceivable that the beginner might confuse certain mature specimens with the dangerous *Amanita pantherina*.

However, I must in fairness add that although *A. rubescens*

73 *Amanita rubescens* (young sporophore)

74   *Amanita rubescens* (mature sporoph

is indigestible when raw, it has long been regarded as a delicacy after cooking, when the irritant properties are lost.

To ensure the complete removal of the astringent properties, it is preferable to fry the specimens rather than to stew them in a closed pan.

The flavour is in itself rather tart, but the piquancy imparts an interesting tang to the more bland flavour of many other fungi, if a single cap of blusher is quartered and mixed in before cooking. It is generally recommended that the caps are first peeled, and that they are parboiled, discarding the juice, before frying.

The Rev. Worthington G. Smith, of whom I have made mention elsewhere, assures in his usual flamboyant fashion that he well knows the fungus 'to be delicious and perfectly wholesome, as I have not only eaten it myself, but have known it to be eaten largely by many amateurs'.

ARMILLARIA MELLEA (Vahl. ex Fr.) Kümmer. Honey fungus.

Habitat: parasitic on a wide variety of living trees both coniferous and frondose, causing serious destruction; also sapro–phytic on stumps and submerged roots, thus the sporophore may erroneously appear to be growing on soil. Typically caespitose, rarely solitary.

Dimensions: cap 5–15 cm. dia.; stipe 5–10 cm. tall x 1.0–2.5 cm. dia.

Cap: at first brown, later as the cap expands honey coloured, with dark brown fibrillose squamules, thinning out from the centre, at first erect then flaccid. At first hemispherical, becoming flatly conical, and finally plano–expanded to depressed, with incurved margin. Flesh fulvous; spongy in mature specimens. The whole colony typically takes on a white dusty appearance when mature, from covering with spores.

Gills: at first off–white, then fulvous, typically with dark brown spots in older specimens, finally dusted white with spores. Arcuate–decurrent, terminating proximally at a definite line on the stem; thin and subdistant. Spores hyaline, white in the mass, ovate, smooth, 7–10 x 5–6 μ.

Stipe: paler than cap, darkening to brown at base; fibrillose, elastic and flexuose, slightly furrowed; becoming bulbous at the base. Annulus whitish; sulcate on upper surface, thick, membraneous. Flesh cartilaginous. Sporophores connected to black 'boot–lace' rhizomorphs by which the colony spreads vegetatively.

Odour: unpleasantly acidic when fresh.

Occurrence: very common. August–November.

Armillaria mellea (young sporoph

77   *Armillaria mellea* (mature sporophores)

As soon as this fungus appears each year, I make an immediate sortie to the woods and collect a mountain of juicy young specimens for a gluttonous gorge. I view the moment with much the same pleasurable anticipation as the first crop of summer strawberries and always force the ritual on any hapless friends and relatives who happen to be about at the time.

I have never suffered ill–effects from this extravaganza, nor have the people who gallantly shared my banquets. Once I even managed to persuade a party of highly sceptical teachers on a field–study course to sample the delights of honey fungus, and to my knowledge none regretted the experience. The specimen is much sought after on the Continent, particularly in Switzerland, where because of its strong flavour it is used as a condiment. However, in this country it has received mixed acclaim, perhaps unfairly. The most off–putting characteristic of honey fungus is its distinctly acid odour when fresh. I remember the first occasion when I brought some of the specimens home for cooking. I buried my nose in the basket and took a deep breath, expecting to be regaled with familiar mushroom odour. My immediate reaction was 'this can't be right'. However, after consulting all available textbooks and preparing myself for a speedy end, I went ahead and threw half a dozen caps into the pan. Almost at once the acid smell disappeared, and I was relieved to find this replaced by a mouth–watering rich mushroom aroma, as the specimens cooked through.

There are one or two tips worth following to get the best out of this fungus. Its flavour is very rich and tends to get over–powering as the specimen grows older, so only select fresh–looking material, which feels firm to the touch. Never use specimens that are turning soggy or badly discoloured.

I do not advocate stewing, but if you do adopt this method of cooking, then leave the lid off the pan to allow the acid smell to dissipate.

For me, there is only one way to prepare honey fungus, and that is to cook it gently in butter. Remove the caps and chop the larger ones in halves or quarters. Cut off and discard an inch or so of the bottom of the stalks, then slice down the middle. Throw into a pan with plenty of butter and sauté gently for about ten minutes. The flavour is strong and spicy in itself, and personally I feel there is no need to use any additional condiments. If you find the texture still a little tough, extend the cooking time and reduce the heat.

C. D. Badham, in his book *Esculent Funguses of England*, scathingly described the honey fungus as 'nauseous and disagreeable however cooked'. I suspect that Mr Badham's experience of the fungus never got beyond the collecting stage, and that he was put off by the raw smell. I should in all fairness conclude by stressing that although the fungus is quite digestible for me and has been for all the people I have tried it out on, some individuals do find it too rich, so it is worth experimenting with small amounts at first. Otherwise, this is one of the truly delicious experiences of eating fungi and is definitely not to be missed.

CLITOCYBE FLACCIDA (Sow. ex Fr.) Kümmer.

Habitat: typically in coniferous woods, but may also be found occasionally under frondose trees; gregarious at times, rarely caespitose, typically solitary; on soil.
Dimensions: cap 5–8 cm. dia.; stipe 3–5 cm. tall x 0.5–1.5 cm. dia.
Cap: reddish brown or hazel brown, occasionally more orange or ochraceous; at first convex and depressed at disc, becoming infundibuliform, with expanded slightly flexuose margin, no central umbo; cuticle slightly hygrophanous and darker in damp weather, typically dry and glabrous. Flesh off–white, becoming slightly tinged cap colour with age.
Gills: off–white to cream colour, becoming brown spotted with age, deeply decurrent, narrow, crowded. Spores hyaline, white in the mass, sub–spherical, slightly verrucose 3–5 μ.
Stipe: concolorous with cap, but paler; fibrillose–striate, slightly attenuated upwards, and white tomentose at the base. Flesh off–white, sub–fibrillar, at first full, becoming stuffed floccose, and finally hollow.
Odour: not distinctive. **Taste:** astringent, faintly bitter.
Occurrence: common. September–November.

An advantage of this fungus is that quite a lot tend to grow together and a meal can be collected without too much difficulty.

One of the problems, however, is its rather acid taste. But this can be of advantage, and there is one really piquant recipe using this fungus, which was tried out on me, and which is truly delicious.

Slice the caps and stalks fairly thinly, and sauté in $\frac{1}{2}$ oz. butter with plenty of salt and pepper. Mix together 1 desertspoonful of flour with a little water and a teaspoonful of marmite or yeast extract in a cup, to make a paste, then add $\frac{1}{2}$ pint water, and a liberal volume of Worcester sauce. Add the sauce to the sliced portions and allow to thicken by cooking gently. Try this with roast beef, and I guarantee that the horseradish sauce will be relegated to the back of the shelf for a while!

The acid flavour also lends itself to pickling or ketchup making, so this is quite a versatile fungus and definitely not to be overlooked if you happen to be partial to pleasantly tart flavours in your cooking.

Clitocybe fla

CLITOCYBE GEOTROPA (Bull. ex St. Amans.) Quél.

Habitat: light woods both frondose and coniferous, in grassy clearings, fire breaks, margins of woods, favouring rich calcareous soil; gregarious or scattered, often in rings; on soil.

Dimensions: cap 10–15 cm. dia.; stipe 11–16 cm. tall x 1.5–2.5 cm. dia.

Cap: buff to alutaceous, occasionally tinged pinkish; at first convex becoming flattened, shallowly depressed at disc with small, acute umbo, margin at first involute becoming shallowly scalloped and more or less plane; cuticle dry, matt, glabrous. Flesh off–white, firm, medium fleshy.

Gills: concolorous with cap or slightly paler, decurrent, more or less distant, thick. Spores hyaline, white in the mass, sub–spherical, smooth, 7–9 x 4.5–6.5 μ.

Stipe: concolorous with cap, smooth, slightly attenuated upwards, tomentose or finely velvety below. Flesh off–white, firm, rather fibrillose, medium fleshy.

Odour: reminiscent of almonds.

Occurrence: fairly common. September–November.

CLITOCYBE NEBULARIS (Batsch. ex Fr.) Kümmer. Clouded agaric.

Habitat: woods generally, but more common under conifers; gregarious, often caespitose; on soil.

Dimensions: cap 6–15 cm. dia.; stipe 6–11 cm. tall x 2–3 cm. dia.

Cap: pale greyish brown when dry, darker smokey grey when wet; at first convex, becoming plano–expanded to slightly depressed, with slightly flexuose margin in older specimens; cuticle generally glabrous but may be slightly pruinose towards disc. Flesh white, thick.

Gills: white or slightly cream, slightly decurrent, narrow, crowded. Spores hyaline, white in the mass, ellipsoidal, smooth, 5–8 x 3–4 μ.

Stipe: white, fibrillose, striate, and slightly attenuated towards apex. Flesh white, firm when young, becoming more soft and spongy, thick.

Odour: very slight, sickly sweetish.

Occurrence: common. August–November.

It is advisable to select only really fresh–looking specimens as the older caps are typically wormy and popular with slugs,

Clitocybe neb

snails and beetles.

The flavour of the fungus when cooked is aromatic, and some find it indigestible. However, for those with strong constitutions, it makes an excellent dish. At one time it was popularly known as the new cheese agaric, because the odour of the fresh specimen was reportedly like that of cottage cheese, although its likeness to the odour of this particular fungus is lost on me.

This is an excellent specimen to stew, and then prepare a white sauce from the juices, as the flavour is sufficiently strong to carry through the sauce. Frying with breadcrumbs after dipping slices of the cap in egg is a pleasant alternative. On the Continent the flavour is considered by many to be too strong on its own, and the fungus is popular mixed with other, more bland–tasting specimens.

CLITOCYBE ODORA (Bull. ex Fr.) Kümmer. Sweet agaric; Anise agaric; Fragrant agaric.

Habitat: typically in deciduous woods, favouring beech; also recorded in coniferous woods; typically gregarious; among leaf litter on soil.

Dimensions: cap 4–8 cm. dia.; stipe 3–8 cm. tall x 1.0–1.5 cm. dia.

Cap: bluish grey–green, or more verdigris green when young; less typically, slaty grey or pallid green; at first convex becoming expanded to irregularly flattened, finally slightly depressed with shallow umbo, and flexuose to lobate at the margin; cuticle smooth, glabrous. Flesh pale bluish green, more or less concolorous with cap cuticle.

Gills: slightly paler than cap cuticle, otherwise concolorous; decurrent, broad, crowded, thin. Spores hyaline, white in the mass, ellipsoidal, smooth 7–9 x 4–5 μ.

Stipe: concolorous with gills, typically shortish, glabrous, sometimes clavate below, and typically flexuose, whitely tomentose at the base (may travel horizontally through leaf litter for 1–2 cm.) Flesh pallid green, at first full, becoming floccose stuffed, to hollow, medium.

Odour: strongly aromatic, smelling of aniseed.

Occurrence: quite common. August–October.

A not unattractive fungus with quite distinctive colouring, but the spicy aniseed smell is what really gives it away.

Here is a specimen, too strong to use by itself, that is excel–

Clitocybe a

lently suited to flavouring. One or two caps in a dish of more bland–flavoured fungi will effectively produce a pleasant aromatic tang.

The aniseed smell is well retained during both drying and storage, and the fungus can be chopped or ground up to add to soups and stews.

CLITOPILUS PRUNULUS (Scop. ex Fr.) Kümmer. Plum agaric.

Habitat: frondose and coniferous woods, typically at edges of woodland paths, on mossy banks etc; solitary or loosely scattered; on soil.

Dimensions: cap 3–6 cm. dia.; stipe 3–6 cm. tall x 1.0–2.0 cm. dia.

Cap: white, finally becoming slightly greyish pink; at first hemispherical, becoming pulvinate with involute margin, and finally irregularly expanded to depressed with flexuose margin, which may still be slightly involute; cuticle finely pruinose or velvety, dry, smooth, may be slightly viscid when wet. Flesh white, soft, medium.

Gills: off–white at first, becoming tinged greyish pink, deeply decurrent, crowded, narrow. Spores hyaline, pale pink in the mass, fusiform, with six characteristic longitudinal ridges, 11–14 x 4–6 μ.

Stipe: off–white, short, may be eccentric, attenuated down–wards, tomentose at the base, otherwise fibrillose furrowed, and slightly pruinose above. Flesh white, soft.

Odour: farinose. **Taste:** farinose.

Occurrence: common. August–November.

The redoubtable Worthington Smith reports making pilgrimages to woods 'north of London' for this 'delicious morsel', which he apparently regarded as something of a rarity. A popular Victorian recipe for the fungus was cooking with mince, or fricasseeing. They also used it to improve the flavour of vol–au–vents.

It has generally been regarded as an extremely savoury specimen. One interesting variation which I turned up for making a dish of the fungus alone is to serve it with 'Sterbeck's white sauce'. To prepare this (no quantities are available), mix some ground almond to a paste with a little water, then add salt, pepper and lemon juice, and use the resulting mixture as a condiment, like ordinary mustard.

COPRINUS COMATUS (Müll. ex Fr.) Gray.
Judge's wig; Shaggy ink cap.

Habitat: typically in grass of roadside verges, but also appearing generally in pastures; gregarious; on soil.

Dimensions: cap 5–14 cm. high, varying in diameter with expansions; stipe 7–15 cm. tall x 1.5–2.5 cm. dia.

Cap: white; at first ovate, adpressed to stipe at the margin, soon becoming conical–campanulate, expanded below; cuticle shaggy with feathery, imbricate scales, except at extreme apex which is typically smooth. Flesh white, delicate, medium. Cap autodigests from margin, becoming brown, finally black and deliquescent, leaving a small, flat vestige at the disc, with revolute margin.

Gills: at first wholly white, becoming pink, brown, and finally black; free, ventricose crowded. Spores black sub–ellipsoidal, smooth, 8–14 x 6–8 μ.

Stipe: wholly white, smooth, rapidly elongating; annulus at first conspicuous, fugacious, fairly low on stipe; base of stipe rather bulbous, solid, lacking volval remains. Flesh white, delicate hollow even when young, medium.

Odour: slightly acid, but disappearing on cooking.

Occurrence: very common. June–October.

The judge's wig holds a special place among edible fungi for me, because, as far as I can remember, it was the first toad–stool I ever tasted.

Although some people pass it by as lacking in flavour, I must hasten to its defence as an excellent dish, providing it is cooked in the right manner for such a delicate specimen. The fungus is fleshy and all parts can be employed for cooking. One essential prerequisite is that the specimens are collected in prime condition and utilised immediately. Ideally the gills should be pure white, or at most bearing a trace of pink. Discard any specimens where the gills have started to go brown or black, as chemical changes equivalent to putrefaction will have occurred in the tissue.

It has been advocated that the scales be carefully scraped away before cooking, but this is quite unnecessary and only spoils the pretty appearance of the cap. You may find that the apex of the cap is discoloured and that particles of soil are adhering in places. In that case scrape or brush off the offending areas so that the specimens are clean. Also remove the base of the stalk. Next, slice the caps lengthways in quarters, having first removed the stalks, and halve the stalks lengthways.

The texture of the fungus is very tender, and consequently it only requires the gentlest of cooking. The simplest recipe is

Coprinus comatus

gently sautéing in butter with a dash of salt and pepper. However, for the more adventuresome, I would strongly recommend the following:

1 lb. ink caps sliced as described above

2 oz. butter

1 cup white wine

pinch of nutmeg

seasoning

croutons

Sauté the fungi very gently for 10 minutes in butter in a saucepan. Put in a casserole dish and add the wine and seasoning. Mix well and top with squares of bread. Bake at 350°F in the oven until the croutons are brown.

The effect of the addition of wine is to add just the right amount of interest to the rather mild flavour of the ink caps.

Truly delicious!

CORTINARIUS ALBO–VIOLACEOUS (Pers. ex Fr.) Fr.

Habitat: in frondose woods, favouring oak and beech; scattered or loosely gregarious; on soil.

Dimensions: cap 3–8 cm. dia.; stipe 3–8 cm. tall x 2.0–2.5 cm. dia.

Cap: wholly lilac blue, becoming paler in older specimens; at first convex–campanulate, becoming plane, and bluntly umbonate; cuticle smooth, silky shining, with marginal striations. Flesh off–white, becoming tinged cap colour; moderately fleshy.

Gills: at first pale grey, with faint violaceous blue tinge, becoming cinnamon brown with spore dust; at first covered with whitish grey cobwebby veil or cortina, connate to stipe; adnate, distant. Spores cinnamon brown, ovate, smooth 9.0 x 5.5 μ.

Stipe: concolorous with cap; smooth, silky shining, clavate, typically white sheathed to cortina, which is fugacious. Flesh off–white tinged violaceous blue towards apex.

Odour: not distinctive.

Occurrence: fairly frequent. August–October.

A somewhat prosaic Victorian remarked of this fungus: 'a most exquisitely rich luxury, much resembling the meadow mushroom in flavour, but altogether firmer, more meaty, and substantial.'

Further comment would only be superfluous!

FLAMMULINA VELUTIPES (Curt. ex Fr.) Karst.

Habitat: either parasitic or saprophytic, on the trunks and stumps of frondose trees, occasionally on higher branches; crowded caespitose.

Dimensions: cap 2–7 cm. dia.; stipe 3–9 cm. tall x 0.5–1.0 cm. dia.

Cap: yellowish tan, paling to cream at the margin, and darker orange brown at disc; at first convex then expanded–irregular; cuticle glabrous and viscid when moist. Flesh pallid, thin, particularly at the margin.

Gills: at first pallid then tinted cream to pale tan; adnexed, ventricose and rounded proximally; rather distant. Spores cream, hyaline, ellipsoidal, smooth 8–10 x 3–5 μ.

Stipe: dark chestnut brown except immediately under cap, where more tan colour; central or slightly eccentric to cap; densely velvety, rooting. Flesh pallid, full at first, becoming hollow.

Odour: not distinctive.

Occurrence: common, September–December; occasional, January and February.

Flammulina is a strongly flavoured fungus and is hardly likely to be confused with any other species on account of its very characteristic dark velvety stems.

Many people regard the taste as too piquant on its own, in addition to which the caps are not particularly fleshy and the stems are definitely tough. However, the fungus is well worth drying for use as a condiment. String through the caps and hang in a warm dry place; when thoroughly leathery, chop both caps and stems as small as possible for a useful addition to your store of herbs.

Incidentally, it is also worth adding a few fresh caps to a stew or casserole. However, for an idea to impress (or horrify) your dinner guests, how about using the caps as a basis for a creamed soup?

Take about a dozen fresh caps and sauté them in butter with a small chopped onion; after a few minutes add two ounces of

Flammulina velut

plain flour and cook for a further minute; stir in one pint of milk and one pint of chicken stock (or water), and bring to the boil; season with paprika pepper and salt, and simmer gently for about five minutes; add one cupful dry white wine; serve immediately with croutons and garnish with parsley. If you want to go the whole hog, then include a small pot of double cream at the last minute!

GALERINA MUTABILIS (PHOLIOTA) *(Schaeff. ex Fr.) Orton. *Kümmer.

Habitat: saprophytic on stumps of frondose trees, less frequently on dead lower parts of living trees; typically caespitose.

Dimensions: cap 2–6 cm. dia.; stipe 4–8 cm. tall x 0.4–0.7 cm. dia.

Cap: hygrophanous, date brown when wet, drying from the disc to pale ochrous tan, thus typically pale tan at disc with darker marginal belt; at first campanulate, becoming expanded–convex, with or without low umbo; cuticle smooth, glabrous, slightly viscid when wet. Flesh dirty white, fairly firm, medium.

Gills: at first pale brown or clay, ageing to cinnamon or rust brown; weakly decurrent to adnate, crowded, covered by pellicular veil when young. Spores pale brown, ovate, smooth 6–7 x 3–4 μ.

Stipe: bearing dark brown annulus, pale brown above annulus, glabrous, and finely sulcate, dark brown below annulus and minutely squamulose. Flesh rust brown, firm, medium.

Odour: strong, not distinctive.

Occurrence: fairly frequent. June–November.

I suppose it is possible to confuse this specimen with *Armillaria mellea*, the honey fungus, but since the latter is also an excellent table specimen, there can be no serious consequence to such an error.

G. mutabilis makes a worthy addition to soups and stews due to its strong flavour. For just this reason, I do not advocate its use as a separate dish, although a desirable concoction might be produced by stewing the fungus and preparing it with a lemon sauce, in the same way as oyster cap. When cooked, the specimens give off a delicious pervading aroma. It could also be tried chopped small and added to mince for an extra sparkle.

All in all, providing you can find the specimens in the first place, which is not always easy, this fungus has adequate flavour

91

Galerina mut

to be versatile in use. One advantage is that it tends to appear quite early in the season, when other material may not be so readily available.

HYGROPHORUS EBURNEUS (LIMACIUM) *(Bull. ex Fr.) *Kümmer.

Habitat: frondose woods generally; solitary but typically prolific within a location; on soil.

Dimensions: cap 3–6 cm. dia.; stipe 6–10 cm. tall x 0.75–1.0 cm. dia.

Cap: wholly white, or with slight ivory tinge, never olivaceous; at first convex, becoming expanded and bluntly umbonate; cuticle somewhat glutinous in damp weather, otherwise dry shining, smooth, glabrous. Flesh white, firm, thick in the umbo, otherwise fairly thin.

Gills: white, decurrent, thick, distant. Spores hyaline, white in the mass, ellipsoidal, smooth, 8–9 x 5–6 μ.

Stipe: white, farinose to minutely squamulose above, thickly glutinous below, particularly in damp weather; may be attenuated slightly downwards. Flesh white, fibrillar, at first full, becoming floccose stuffed and finally hollow, medium.

Odour: not distinctive.

Occurrence: common and at times prolific. August–November.

All members of the *Hygrophorus* genus are edible, though none are of outstanding worth. One of their most distinctive characteristics is the broad spacing of the gills, which are white and tend to have a thick, waxy feel about them.

I have selected two species, as representative of the family, because in my experience they are among the most common. Certainly I have seen *H. eburneus* so prolific in some localities during the autumn that one could hardly avoid walking on them. It can be easily confused with two related white species, *H. chrysaspis,* and *H. niveus,* though the latter is a grassland species, and the former gives a brown reaction with potassium hydroxide, which *H. eburneus* does not. However, since all are edible, there is no problem over possible mistaken identity.

HYGROPHORUS PUNICEUS Fr.

Habitat: pastures, grassy waste places etc; in small groups; on soil.

Dimensions: cap 4–8 cm. dia.; stipe 5–10 cm. tall x 1.5–2.5 cm. dia.

Cap: at first wholly blood red, soon fading to yellowish orange, or tan at the disc; at first campanulate, becoming convex–conical, with flexuose or irregularly lobate margin; cuticle viscid when moist, typically damp, otherwise smooth, glabrous. Flesh concolorous, fragile, thin.

Gills: concolorous with cap but somewhat paler, adnate to free, thick, distant, with somewhat waxy feel when young. Spores hyaline, white in the mass, ovate, smooth, 8–12 x 5–6 μ.

Stipe: concolorous with cap cuticle, but typically more yellowish, white tomentose at base, fibrillose, longitudinally wrinkled, irregular. Flesh concolorous, full, fibrillar, thick.

Odour: not distinctive.

Occurrence: common. August–October.

HYGROPHOROPSIS AURANTIACA ([Wulf.] Fr.) Maire apud Martin–Sano. False chantarelle.

Habitat: coniferous woods and heaths; gregarious or loosely scattered; on soil.

Dimensions: cap 2–6 cm. dia.; stipe 3–6 cm. tall x 0.4–0.8 cm. dia.

Cap: wholly orange, or egg yellow, becoming paler ochrous when dry; at first pulvinate with inrolled margin, becoming plano–convex, or depressed at the disc, finally irregular plane, with undulating margin; cuticle dull, glabrous. Flesh pale orange, spongy soft, thin.

Gills: deep orange, decurrent, fairly shallow, crowded, forked but never anastomosing, often wavy crisped when dry. Spores hyaline, cream colour in the mass, ovate, smooth 6–7 x 4–5 μ. Give dextrinoid reaction with Melzer's Iodine.

Stipe: concolorous with cap, slightly attenuated towards the base, finely tomentose; typically curved at base; flesh rather tough, at first full, becoming hollow, thin.

Odour: not distinctive. **Taste:** sickly acrid.

Occurrence: prolific. August–November.

I have included this fungus here, not because of any culinary worth but because it can very easily be confused with the true chantarelle *(Cantharellus cibarius)*. Some old reference books used to list *H. aurantiaca* as poisonous. However, I must stress that it is quite harmless, should you inadvertently include it in your dish of chantarelles, or even cook a whole potful in error. The taste is totally uninteresting—apart from wondering whatever hap-

94

Hygrophorus eburneus

Hygrophorus pur

Hygrophoropsis aurantiaca

pened to your delicious chantarelles, you will assuredly wake up in fine fettle next morning!

The fungi do differ in certain essential respects: firstly, *Cantharellus* does not possess true gills—there is quite an obvious difference between the true 'knife edge' gills of *Hygrophoropsis* and the shallow, blunt ridges of *Cantharellus*; secondly, if you are still uncertain, look closely at the forking of the gills, because, although in both forms there is an obvious outward branching, it is only in *Cantharellus* that the forks ever anastomose or join up again. Apart from these differences, the 'feel' of a chantarelle is much more fleshy than the rather thin, delicate construction of the other.

LACCARIA AMETHYSTINA (Bull. ex Mérat) Murrill.
Amethyst agaric.

Habitat: frondose woods; solitary or scattered; on soil.
Dimensions: cap 1–5 cm. dia.; stipe 3–7 cm. tall x 2–5 mm. dia.
Cap: variable in colour, often pale greyish or whitish when dry, deep violet or amethyst when moist; at first convex, becoming typically umbilicate at centre, with flexuose, revolute margin; less frequently remaining shallowly convex; cuticle at first glabrous, smooth, becoming slightly farinose. Flesh concolorous with cap, thin.
Gills: deep violet, becoming dusted with white spores. Adnate to slightly decurrent, broad, distant, and thick. Spores hyaline, white in the mass, spherical, aculeate, 7–10 μ.
Stipe: concolorous with cap, striate, fibrous–elastic, slightly flexuose. Flesh concolorous, fibrillar, firm, thin.
Odour: not distinctive.
Occurrence: very common. August–November.

LACCARIA LACCATA (Scop. ex Fr.) Cooke.

Habitat: woods and heaths; solitary or scattered; on soil.
Dimensions: cap 1–6 cm. dia.; stipe 3–10 cm. tall x 2–8 cm. dia.
Cap: very variable in colour, ranging from pale greyish cream when dry, to hazel or rufous when moist. At first convex, becoming typically umbilicate at centre, with flexuose, revolute margin, less frequently remaining shallowly convex; cuticle at first glabrous, smooth becoming slightly farinose. Flesh paler than cap colour and thin.
Gills: flesh colour, becoming dusted with white spores; adnate

Laccaria amethystina

Laccaria la

to slightly decurrent, broad, distant, and thick. Spores white, hyaline, spherical, aculeate 7–10 μ.

Stipe: concolorous with cap, and of very variable length according to immediate surroundings of the fruiting body, e.g. longer in grass than on bare woodland floor. Striate, fibrous–elastic, slightly flexuose. Flesh concolorous, fibrillar, firm, thin.

Odour: not distinctive.

Occurrence: very common. August–November.

As will readily be observed from the foregoing descriptions of the *Laccaria* fungi they are biologically very similar, but they can also be conveniently coupled from a culinary viewpoint, since their taste and edibility is more or less identical.

L. amethystina must surely be one of the prettiest small fungi to grace our woodlands, but it can easily be overlooked. In anything but really damp weather, the cap colour is an incon–spicuous buff, and one has to pick the specimen and turn it over to gain the full impression of the really intense violet colour from which it gains its popular name.

Neither of the specimens is of outstanding worth for eating, largely because of the tough stringy stalks, which should be discarded, and the lack of any real substance to the cap. However, both types are extremely prolific in most years and may rescue one from the gloomy prospect of going home empty handed when other specimens are sparse.

Here is one interesting little recipe which I feel lends itself quite well to either of the *Laccariae*:

6 tbs. chopped ham

$\frac{1}{2}$ lb. *Laccaria* caps

8 eggs

1 cup chicken stock

1 oz. butter

3 tbs. sherry

nutmeg

Melt the butter in a saucepan, and add the mushrooms, ham and stock. Cook for 5 minutes over a high flame to reduce the liquid, then reduce the heat, add the sherry, and simmer for a further 10 minutes. Break in the eggs, cover and allow the eggs to cook through for a further 5–6 minutes. Add a dash of nutmeg before serving. (serves 4)

LACTARIUS DELICIOSUS (L. ex Fr.) Gray. Saffron milk cap.

Habitat: coniferous woods, favouring spruce; solitary; on soil.

Dimensions: cap 5–12 cm. dia.; stipe 6–10 cm. tall x 2.0–2.5 cm. dia.

Cap: dull reddish orange with darker and lighter concentric zones, occasionally with green tinge; in older specimens the whole cap may take on a dull, greenish grey colour; at first convex with strongly involute margin, becoming expanded to depressed, though tending to remain involute; cuticle at first minutely tomen–tose, becoming glabrous and dull, but slightly viscid in damp weather. Flesh concolorous, firm, medium.

Gills: concolorous with cap, but turning green where bruised; adnexed, broad, crowded, rather brittle. Spores off–white, cream with pinkish tinge in the mass, spherical to ovate, briefly echinate, 8–10 x 7–8 μ.

Stipe: concolorous with cap, also discolouring green; smooth, glabrous. Flesh slightly paler, particularly in young specimens; at first full, becoming stuffed and finally hollow, medium.

All parts yield milky latex, immediately turning reddish orange.

Odour: aromatic. **Taste:** bitter.

Occurrence: fairly frequent. August–November.

This was one of those species over whose inclusion I was in two minds.

I have tried eating it, and unless one is careful about the cooking, the taste is definitely bitter. For this reason I would not advocate stewing, as some Victorian authors suggest. However, there is a general weight of opinion in favour of the fungus as a good edible specimen, and apparently there are no records of anyone becoming ill after eating it.

I would think that the best approach to cooking L. deliciosus (the name is incentive enough to experiment!) is simply to sauté thoroughly, and then dress with something like lemon juice, after which the bitter taste, if it still remains, is well disguised.

According to C. D. Badham, in his *Esculent Funguses of England,* the species was 'exhibited in prodigious quantities' in the open markets of Marseilles about a hundred years ago.

Lactarius deliciosus

He described the fungus as 'very luscious eating, full of rich gravy, with a little of the flavour of mussels'. I can't help feeling, with regard to the last comment, that either Dr Badham had a vivid imagination or that there were shellfish from that Marseilles market in his shopping bag too, because I cannot taste the remotest resemblance to mussels in a dish of *Lactarius deliciosus*!

Badham advocates baking the caps, with a pat of butter on each, and well seasoned, in a closely covered pie dish for ¾ hour; alternatively stew and serve with white sauce made from the juice.

These fungi can readily be used in ketchup but are unsuitable for drying as they deteriorate in the process.

LACTARIUS VOLEMUS (Fr.) Fr. Tawny milk cap.

Habitat: mixed woods; solitary; on soil.

Dimensions: cap 8–12 cm. dia.; stipe 5–10 cm. tall x 1.5–2.5 cm. dia.

Cap: tawny brown or tawny orange, varying towards more yellowish brown in some specimens; at first convex, becoming plano–convex depressed weakly at disc, with involute margin; cuticle pruinose or minutely velvety at first, becoming wholly glabrous smooth, dull, dry, often cracked irregularly in older specimens. Flesh pallid or yellowish with abundant latex, which turns greyish brown after exposure to air for a few minutes; flesh hard, brittle, medium.

Gills: cream colour or pale yellow, later brown spotted with latex; adnate to weakly decurrent, crowded, thick, hard. Spores pallid, cream colour in the mass, sub–globose, minutely spinulose and ribbed 8–12 x 7–11 μ.

Stipe: concolorous with cap, but whitish and finely pruinose above at first, slowly becoming wholly smooth; sub–cylindrical or ventricose. Flesh pallid or yellowish, hard, full, medium.

Odour: at first not distinctive, but later smelling moderately of fish.

Occurrence: occasional. August–October.

This, the only other species of *Lactarius* generally considered worth eating, is popularly known in Switzerland as the fryling, It is interesting to note that, as well as sautéed, the fungus is eaten raw, by marinating in lemon and oil, and dishing up as an hors–d'oeuvre with mayonnaise.

The very distinctive colour is probably the main distinguish–

ing characteristic. The only poisonous species with which it might possibly be confused is *L. helvus* whose colour is considerably less orange and definitely café–au–lait.

LEPIOTA PROCERA (Scop. ex Fr.) Gray. Parasol mushroom.

Habitat: edges of forests, grassy clearings, firebreaks, gardens etc; solitary; on soil.
Dimensions: cap: 10–23 cm. dia.; stipe 15–30 cm. tall x 1.5–2.0 cm. dia.
Cap: at first dull brown, but as cap expands cuticle breaks up into greyish brown imbricate scales, with white flesh showing in the cracks, except at disc which remains wholly brown and smooth; at first ovoid–spherical, becoming conical and finally expanded–conical or slightly umbonate. Flesh white, at first firm, and dry, becoming floccose, unchanging, thick.
Gills: white, unchanging, free and slightly distant, broad, ventricose, and crowded. Spores hyaline, white in the mass, ellip–soidal, smooth 15–20 x 10–13 μ.
Stipe: at first greyish brown, later breaking up into concentric scaly belts with white flesh showing in the cracks; very tall comparative to cap diameter, with moveable annulus in upper third; annulus white on top but concolorous with stipe below, stiff, two layered, with frayed lower margin; base of stipe thickened into prominent bulb; stipe easily detached from cap. Flesh white, stuffed floccose becoming hollow, fibrillar and woody in mature specimens, thick.
Odour: not distinctive.
Occurrence: frequent on good years. July–October.

See *L. rhacodes* for suggestions on cooking, etc.

LEPIOTA RHACODES (Vitt.) Quél. Shaggy parasol.

Habitat: mixed woods, parks, gardens, favouring rich soil; solitary or in small groups; on soil.
Dimensions: cap 6–15 cm. dia.; stipe 12–16 cm. tall x 1.0–1.5 cm. dia.
Cap: cuticle broken up into large imbricate scales, at first clay brown, darkening to almost black, with dirty white flesh showing through; at first sub–spherical, becoming campanulate, sometimes more conical, and finally plano–expanded with slight central umbo, darker than the rest of cap. Flesh off–white, rufescent where cut, thick.

Lepiota pro

Lepiota rhacodes var. *hortensis*

Gills: white, may be slightly rufous at the edges in older specimens; rufescent where bruised; free, slightly distant from stipe, broad, narrowing proximally, somewhat crowded. Spores hyaline, white in the mass, ellipsoidal, longitudinally wrinkled 10–12 x 6–7 μ.

Stipe: dirty white, smooth, at first often whitish floccose under cap; annulus two–layered, white, moveable, floccose–fibrillose, may become detached; base of stipe bulbous, becoming gradually attenuated towards apex. Flesh white, fibrillar, hollow, woody, thick. Cap easily detached from stipe.

Odour: pleasantly aromatic.

Occurrence: occasional, more frequent in some years. August–November.

Despite certain features reminiscent of the dangerous *Amanita* group, including an annulus and a bulbous base, this fungus is a highly distinctive specimen. The imbricate scales are quite unlike the white velar patches on *Amanita* caps, and the only specimen which is likely to cause confusion is the parasol mushroom, *Lepiota procera*. As luck would have it, this related specimen is also excellent for eating, so both can be collected with confidence.

The only real drawback to either fungus is that they have rather tough stringy stems. It is, therefore, best to discard these and use only the large fleshy caps.

When the caps are young and bell–shaped, they make attractive receptacles for practically any sort of savoury filling that takes your fancy. Try a tomato for a colourful acorn effect, or fill the cap with mincemeat or vegetable stuffing, such as sage and onion, then cook in the oven for about half an hour. It is best to turn the cap 'right way up' and baste the top with a little beef dripping.

However, this sort of preparation does completely disguise the gently aromatic flavour of the fungus. For those who prefer a more simple approach, I recommend gently broiling with butter and a little salt and pepper. Stand the caps in just enough butter to stop them sticking to the pan, and put a knob of butter inside each. Cover and cook through. The caps can be cooked quite quickly as they tend not to shrink.

My favourite recipe for parasols is one that I myself claim patent rights for, and is a variation on the double–decker sandwich principle. For this epicurean masterpiece, it is essential to obtain caps that are fully expanded. Place these singly in shallow glass baking dishes, add butter and seasoning, and braise. At the same time fry or grill some mild bacon (honey smoked if you can get it) and toast three slices of bread. Place the cooked cap on one layer of toast and the bacon on another, decorate with a sprig of parsley, and you have the finest toasted sandwich you have ever tasted!

Some people advocate scraping off the scales before cooking, but unless there is a lot of soil adhering to the caps, I think this is quite unnecessary and only detracts from the interesting appearance of the fungus when cooked.

LEPISTA NUDA (TRICHOLOMA) *(Bull. ex Fr.) Cooke. *Kümmer. Wood blewit.

Habitat: generally in and around both frondose and coniferous woods; frequently gregarious; on soil.

Dimensions: cap 7–12 cm. dia.; stipe 5–10 cm. tall x 2–3 cm. dia.

Cap: at first lilac, becoming pale greyish violet, or darker brownish violet as the cap expands, generally darker towards disc; at first convex, becoming irregularly expanded, with revolute margin; cuticle hygrophanous in wet weather, otherwise smooth, glabrous and slightly moist. Flesh at first vivid dense lilac, and firm, becoming paler and softer with age, medium but thin at the margin.

Gills: at first densely bluish violet, becoming paler and more flesh coloured; sinuate, deep, crowded, easily separable from flesh of cap. Spores pale lilac, hyaline, ellipsoidal, echinate 7–10 x 4–6 μ.

Stipe: pale greyish violet, often with more dense colour at apex, and terminating at a definite line on the stipe; may be rusty brown tinged at the base; fibrillose–squamulose, may be pruinose at apex, base typically slightly bulbous and often tomentose. Flesh lilac, full, firm.

Odour: not distinctive.

Occurrence: common. September–November.

On a mildly cautionary note, I must first mention that when raw, this fungus contains very small quantities of a haemolysing agent, which attacks red blood cells. However, for this to have much effect one would have to consume quite a large quantity of uncooked specimens, and the poison is completely destroyed on cooking. For safety's sake, however, I would not recommend the use of the fungus in salads.

Having disposed of the only vaguely unsavoury aspect of wood blewits, I hasten to extol their culinary virtues, because they really make excellent eating. In the Midlands, they were once sold regularly at markets during the autumn. They seem particularly prevalent in those counties, and this may account for the fact that their commercial popularity never spread to the South.

As the fungi tend to absorb water readily, they should be picked on a dry day, or they tend to become mushy when cooked.

I have tried to avoid describing so–called 'traditional' recipes for fungi, because I think they are largely over–rated and invariably turn out to be the sort of procedure that any well–versed cook would follow in any case. However, an old recipe for blewits is so extensively quoted that I feel I must bow to convention and include it.

The fungus is traditionally prepared in the same way as 'tripe and onions' and is supposed to offer a vegetarian substitute, on account of the rather gelatinous nature of the flesh when cooked.

Detach the stems from the caps, and chop them finely. Chop up an equal quantity of onion and mix the two together, adding a little sage. Put the caps in a saucepan and add the chopped mixture. Dress with a little bacon fat, and add milk to cover. Simmer for half an hour on a low heat. Pour off the liquid and make this into a white sauce with butter, flour and seasoning. Pour this back over the caps, and simmer gently for another quarter of an hour.

The mixture is traditionally served with mashed potato, apple sauce, and toasted croutons. However, I can't help feeling that one would save oneself an awful lot of trouble by simply buying and cooking proper tripes, because any flavour in the fungus is well and truly smothered by 'sage and onion'.

It is worth trying, if only for the experience of eating a traditional dish, but I much prefer to leave out the highly flavoured ingredients, and simply cook in milk, making a white sauce of the juice with salt and pepper and possibly a little mustard. The pleasantly aromatic taste of the fungus can then be savoured in its own right.

LEPISTA SAEVA (TRICHOLOMA) *(Fr.) Orton. *Gillet. Blewit.

Habitat: open grassy places, in and around frondose woods, also typically in pastures; solitary or in rings; on soil.
Dimensions: cap 7–14 cm. dia.; stipe 5–12 cm. tall x 2.0–3.5 cm. dia.
Cap: pale tan to flesh colour; at first hemispherical, becoming plano–convex with involute margin, and finally expanded with obtuse margin; cuticle at first pruinose, becoming wholly smooth, glabrous, and dull. Flesh white, at first firm,

Lepista nuda

becoming spongy soft.

Gills: wholly flesh colour, sinuate, crowded, broad. Spores hyaline, white in the mass, ellipsoidal, echinate, 7–10 x 4–6 μ.

Stipe: violaceous or bluish grey, at first minutely white tomentose, later with violaceous fibrils or squamules; stout with slightly bulbous base. Flesh pale flesh colour, firm, full.

Odour: not distinctive.

Occurrence: fairly common. October–November.

Culinary details as for *L. nuda*.

MARASMIUS OREADES (Bolt. ex Fr.) Fr. Fairy ring champignon.

Habitat: pastures and lawns, typically forming rings. Can withstand considerable dessication, remaining viable when shrivelled.

Dimensions: cap 2–5 cm. dia.; stipe 3–8 cm. tall x 0.3–0.5 cm. dia.

Cap: pale tan to mid tan, strongly hygrophanous and darker in wet weather; margin always paler than umbo. At first conical, becoming plano–expanded with broad obtuse umbo; cuticle slightly crenulate and striate at margin, particularly in wet weather. Flesh pallid, elastic, thin.

Gills: cream colour, free alternating with shorter inter–mediates; widely spaced, fairly broad and thick, subdistant. Spores cream colour, hyaline, ovate, 8–10 x 4–5 μ.

Stipe: cream to pale tan, at first tomentose becoming glabrous except at the base, rooting. Flesh full, elastic, thin.

Odour: fresh sawdust, occasionally with overtones of bitter almond.

Occurrence: common. May–November.

Note: 'root' often penetrates soil for some distance.

The fairy ring champignon has long been esteemed as of culinary value, because of both its strong flavour and its suit–ability for drying and storing.

Traditionally, the caps are threaded on cotton, using a darning needle, and then hung across the rafters until dry and crisp. The stalks are discarded as they are very tough, although I see no reason why they should not be ground up after drying. The dried caps are a popular condiment on the Continent and, until the last war, could be purchased in French and Italian shops in London. They seem to have now disappeared from the com-

Marasmius oreades

mercial scene, on this side of the Channel at any rate.

The caps provide a tasty dish, either fresh or dried, but they are rather thinly fleshed. Their traditional use in England is as a flavouring for steak and kidney pie, and for soups, although Smith is full of praise for the specimen in its own right, advocating a straightforward broiling in butter—a process guaranteed to produce a flavour 'exquisitely rich and delicious . . . must be tasted to be understood'. However, Smith himself was once caught out by erroneously collecting a similar looking grassland species, and his experience serves as a warning that *M. oreades* must be correctly identified to avoid the possibility of distressing stomach upsets.

Smith collected a specimen which he described as *M. urens*, the false champignon. However, I suspect that this was in fact a *Paneolus* spp., and several of the *Paneolus* group of grassland fungi could conceivably be mistaken for *M. oreades*. In most of these, though, the gills are darker and frequently mottled. Also, they usually grow on dung (though this may not be obvious in a grassy meadow).

Smith's account describes gathering champignons for supper and finding them unusually hot. At first he put this down to the addition of too much pepper by the old woman who cooked them. However, about half an hour after eating he experienced burning sensations in the throat and stomach, accompanied by headache and dizziness. He reported being violently sick for some hours but was none the worse thereafter.

Luckily nothing for which the fungus could readily be mistaken is seriously poisonous, but the illustration serves the theme that care in identification is essential.

PLEUROTIUS OSTREATUS (Jacq. ex Fr.) Kümmer. Oyster cap.

Habitat: parasitic on frondose trees, favouring beech and elm, less common on ash, apple etc, occasionally on coniferous trees, may also appear on fallen trees or boughs, which have come down the previous season; typically imbricate; causes considerable economic damage.

Dimensions: cap 5–15 cm. dia.; stipe up to 5 cm. tall but often rudimentary x 1.5–3.0 cm. dia.

Cap: pale to deep greyish blue, occasionally with brownish tinge, becoming almost black in older specimens; scallop shaped; cuticle waxy, glabrous, sometimes pruinose towards stipe. Flesh whitish, rubbery and thick except at the margin.

Gills: off–white, strongly decurrent, broad, distinct, thick. Spores lilac, hyaline, ellipsoidal–fusiform, 7.5–11.0 x 3.5–5.0 μ.

114

Pleurotius ostreatus

Stipe: eccentric to lateral, off–white, strigose below. Flesh white, tough, full, thick.

Odour: slight, reminiscent of tarragon according to some authorities.

Occurrence: appearing throughout the year, but more common August–December.

Although from time to time I have known intrepid fungus forayers to seize on these specimens and carry them off in triumph to their kitchens, the oyster cap in general seems not to have achieved the acclaim which I think it deserves.

There may be a number of reasons for this. Firstly, I suspect that the fungus is often the subject of mistaken identity with its close relative *Pleurotus dryinus,* which, although not poisonous, is not regarded as good eating. Many people confuse the two species, and, in the season prior to writing this book, I even observed a member of the British Mycological Society leading a foray wrongly identify some caps of *P. dryinus* as the oyster cap. However, the specimens in question were typically off–white and scaly, quite unlike the smooth blue appearance of oyster cap. The mistake was rectified in time, but had it not been, the reputation of an excellent edible fungus would have doubtless fallen one stage lower.

The difficulty in correct identification is not facilitated by the sad fact that pictures of oyster cap in reference books invariably look nothing at all like the real thing. I have chosen the photo–graph reproduced here with some care, as typically characteristic.

A second point of detriment is that the fungus may not look particularly palatable to some people. After all, whoever heard of eating blue mushrooms! Finally, the flesh is rubbery and needs prolonged and careful cooking to render it tender. Personally, I am not averse to the rather tough texture, in much the same way as I enjoy 'blue' steak, but I agree that many people would find it unpalatable.

At any rate, the oyster cap has a fine, strong flavour and is full of delicious juice. It has a slight peppery tang and lends itself to cooking in a variety of ways. However, having enjoyed chicken served in lemon sauce Chinese style, I was tempted to 'lift' the idea and try it out with this fungus.

Cut the caps into convenient slices, having first discarded the rather tough stalks; simmer them in $\frac{1}{2}$ pint of lightly seasoned water in a closed saucepan, until tender. Make up the fluid to $\frac{1}{2}$ pint again, and blend a little of it with 1 dessertspoon of corn–flour. Squeeze half a lemon and add the juice with a teaspoon of sugar to the paste. Blend this with the juice from the fungus and boil to thicken. Pour over the slices and serve with slices of lemon and pieces of fresh lettuce. The lemon enhances the flavour of the fungus and gives the whole dish a delicious piquancy.

PLUTEUS CERVINUS (Schaeff. ex Fr.) Kümmer. Common fawn agaric.

Habitat: on or around the stumps of frondose trees, frequently appearing on recently cut stumps, may be on soil connected to submerged wood by mycelium; solitary or in small groups.

Dimensions: cap 4–10 cm. dia.; stipe 6–10 cm. tall x 1.0–1.5 cm. dia.

Cap: dull greyish brown, with radiating dark brown fibrils, slightly rugose; at first campanulate becoming irregularly expanded; cuticle glabrous, dull when dry, shining in damp weather. Flesh off–white, soft, juicy, thin.

Gills: at first white, becoming tinged flesh colour, and finally more salmon pink; free, ventricose, crowded, broad. Spores pale flesh pink, salmon pink in the mass, sub–spherical, smooth 8–9 x 5–6 μ.

Stipe: pallid with distinctive dark brownish fibrils. Flesh white, soft, full, medium thin.

Odour: not distinctive.

Occurrence: common. March–October.

P. cervinus is of value to the fungus gourmet chiefly because it is available when many other species are not. It appears quite commonly from early spring to the first autumnal frosts.

The taste is not particularly distinctive, but it does stew or sauté well and is worth looking out for.

RUSSULA AERUGINEA Lindbl. ex Fr. Grass green russula.

Habitat: mixed woods, favouring birch, but also occasionally growing in open coniferous woods and on wooded heaths; solitary, or in small groups; on soil.

Dimensions: cap 5–10 cm. dia.; stipe 4–6 cm. tall x 1–2 cm. dia.

Cap: wholly grass–green, occasionally with olive green or yellowish green tinge, darker towards disc; at first convex, soon becoming plano–expanded, and depressed at disc; cuticle glabrous, smooth dull, but viscid in damp weather, sulcate at margin, and separable to $\frac{1}{2}$ or $\frac{3}{4}$ cap diameter. Flesh white, firm, medium fleshy.

Gills: white at first, becoming straw yellow, finally brownish spotted in older specimens; free, rounded at margin, attenuated proximally, thin, very crowded, forked. Spores hyaline, cream

117

Pluteus cerv

Russula aeruginea

colour in the mass, spherical or broadly ellipsoidal, minutely verrucose and briefly echinate 8–9 x 6–7 μ.

Stipe: white, becoming brownish spotted in older specimens, particularly towards base; glabrous, silky shining, with some surface sculpturing. Flesh white, spongy, soft, medium.

Odour: not distinctive.

Occurrence: fairly common. August–October.

The members of the *Russula* genus listed here are all good edible specimens, of medium flavour and pleasant texture. Probably many more species are also perfectly acceptable.

Because many have attractive colours, they are eminently suited for use fresh in salads, with the notable exception of the three species listed in the poisonous section.

The only word of caution I would offer is that they must be collected when young and fresh smelling. Many degenerate when mature, with the emanation of a fishy odour, and these must be strictly avoided.

RUSSULA AURATA (With.) Fr. Golden russula.

Habitat: mixed woods, favouring beech; singly, on soil.

Dimensions: cap 5–9 cm. dia.; stipe 4–8 cm. tall x 1.5–2.5 cm. dia.

Cap: orange to scarlet on golden yellow background; at first sub–spherical, becoming convex and finally depressed at disc, with weakly rounded margin; cuticle at first viscid, but soon dull, dry, smooth or coarsely velvety with tiny flocci, sulcate at margin in mature specimens, and in wet weather only, separable to half cap diameter. Flesh off–white except for up to 4 mm. below cap cuticle which is stained cap colour; at first firm and tenaceous, becoming more brittle and fragile.

Gills: at first pale cream, becoming straw yellow, but bright chrome yellow at the edges; adnexed, broad, fragile. Spores pale yellow, straw yellow in the mass, spherical, verrucose with irregular reticulations, 9–12 μ.

Stipe: white with chrome yellow tinges, especially towards the base; cylindrical, glabrous, with some surface sculpturing. Flesh off–white, at first firm, becoming spongy and lacunose in older specimens.

Odour: not distinctive.

Occurrence: infrequent. August–October.

Russula aurata

RUSSULA CLAROFLAVA Grove.

Habitat: birch woods; solitary or loosely scattered; on soil.
Dimensions: cap 4–12 cm. dia.; stipe 4–10 cm. tall x 1–2 cm. dia.

Cap: golden yellow, chrome yellow, or less frequently more lemon yellow, turning greyish brown where bruised; at first sub–spherical, becoming convex, then plano–convex and slightly depressed at the disc, more infundibuliform in old specimens with obtuse margin; cuticle smooth, dry, shining, glabrous, separable to two–thirds cap diameter, slightly darker towards disc, and slightly sulcate at margin. Flesh at first white, becoming greyish with darker spotting, medium.

Gills: at first ivory colour, becoming more chrome yellow and finally ochraceous, spotted grey; adnexed or free, proximally attenuated, obtuse at the margin, narrow, forked. Spores ochraceous, ovate, echinate with sub–reticular connections, 7–10 x 7–8 μ.

Stipe: at first white, becoming tinged lemon, greyish spotted with age; slight longitudinal surface sculpturing, and attenuated slightly towards base. Flesh white, ageing with darker spotting; at first firm, soon spongy soft, never brittle, medium.

Odour: not distinctive.
Occurrence: frequent. September–October.

RUSSULA CYANOXANTHA (Schaeff ex Secr.) Fr.

Habitat: frondose woods, favouring beech; solitary, or in small groups; on soil.
Dimensions: cap 5–13 cm. dia.; stipe 5–10 cm. tall x 1.5–2.5 cm. dia.

Cap: variable, but generally violaceous blue green with variation towards darker purple, darker green, or general paling; at first convex with revolute margin, becoming convex–expanded and depressed at disc; cuticle glabrous, shining viscid in damp weather, slightly sulcate at margin and extending beyond limit of gills, otherwise radially veined and separable to $\frac{1}{3}$ cap diameter. Flesh white, reddish below cap cuticle; firm, becoming more spongy in older specimens, medium.

Gills: white, adnexed, thin, narrow and attenuated at both ends; flexible and greasy to touch, forked. Spores hyaline, white in the mass, globose with isolated punctation 7–9 μ.

Stipe: white, occasionally with violaceous tinge; cylindrical,

Russula cyanoxantha

smooth, glabrous. Flesh full, firm, becoming slightly spongy in older specimens, medium.
Odour: not distinctive.
Occurrence: common. August–November.

RUSSULA OLIVACEA (Schaeff. ex Secr.) Fr.

Habitat: mixed woods, favouring beech; loosely gregarious; on soil.
Dimensions: cap 10–18 cm. dia.; stipe 6–10 cm. tall x 2.0–3.0 cm. dia.
Cap: somewhat variable in colour, basically wine, or purplish red brown, but varying through olivaceous or ochraceous shades, slightly paler at the margin, and typically with radial zonation (not obvious); at first sub–spherical, becoming convex to flattened and slightly depressed at the disc; cuticle at first glabrous, becoming minutely velvety, and slightly sulcate at margin, partly separable from cap tissue. Flesh at first white, becoming dirty yellow or alutaceous, unchanging; often very wormy.
Gills: at first lemon yellow, becoming wholly egg yellow, adnexed; at first flexible, becoming more stout and brittle; broad, distant and rounded. Spores pale yellow, egg yellow in the mass, large, spherical, (may be slightly ovate) smooth with isolated spines, 8–12 μ.
Stipe: basically white, but flushed purplish pink beneath cap; stoutish, velvety. Flesh concolorous with that of cap, at first firm, becoming more spongy, thick.
Odour: slightly fruity. **Taste:** nutty.
Chemical tests: stipe salmon pink when rubbed with ferrous sulphate crystal; stipe purplish after 10 minutes when treated with 2% aqueous solution of phenol (note: all other *Russula* species turn dull brown with this test).
Occurrence: common. August–October.

This is one of the best of the edible *Russula*, but it is necessary to collect the specimens young, as not only do the caps tend to go mushy but they are extremely prone to infestation by worms and grubs.

124

Russula olivacea

RUSSULA PALUDOSA Britz.

Habitat: in coniferous woods; solitary, or loosely scattered; on soil.

Dimensions: cap 7–14 cm. dia.; stipe 5–10 cm. tall x 2–4 cm. dia.

Cap: typically brick red, darker towards the disc, but may also be tawny orange or ochraceous orange; at first sub–spherical, becoming convex and finally plano–convex, slightly depressed at disc, with obtuse margin; cuticle smooth, shining, viscid, separable wholly, or to ¾ cap diameter, slightly sulcate at margin. Flesh off–white or ivory, unchanging, thick.

Gills: at first off–white, becoming ivory yellow, often tinged cap colour; at first slightly decurrent, becoming adnexed or sinuate, broad, with limited forking. Spores pale yellow, ochraceous in the mass, ovate or ellipsoidal, verrucose–echinate, with reticulations, 8–10 x 7–8 μ.

Stipe: at first white, becoming tinged cap colour; tending to be very stout, ventricose, or clavate at the base, with irregular sculpturing. Flesh off–white, at first firm, then stuffed, thick.

Odour: not distinctive.

Occurrence: more common in northern parts of the British Isles, infrequent in the south. August–October.

RUSSULA PARAZUREA Schaeff.

Habitat: under frondose trees; solitary or in small groups; on soil.

Dimensions: cap 4–8 cm. dia.; stipe 4–5 cm. tall x 0.5–2.0 cm. dia.

Cap: grey–green typically, varying to olive–grey, iron–grey, or azure–grey, shading to brown at disc; at first convex, becoming plane and finally more or less depressed at disc; cuticle faintly pruinose, often becoming satiny at margin, separable to ½ cap diameter. Flesh white, firm, medium.

Gills: white at first, becoming pale creamy yellow; adnexed, fairly distant. Spores hyaline, pale cream colour in the mass, ovate, sub–reticulate, 5.5–8.5 x 5.5–6.5 μ.

Stipe: white typically with yellowish patches at base; sub–cylindrical, widening beneath cap and typically somewhat curved. Flesh white, full, firm at first becoming spongy.

Odour: not distinctive. **Taste:** sweetish.

Occurrence: occasional. August–October.

Russula parazurea

RUSSULA VESCA Fr.

Habitat: typically in frondose woods, favouring oak, recorded under conifers; solitary or scattered; on soil.
Dimensions: cap 4–9 cm. dia.; stipe 5–9 cm. tall x 2–3 cm. dia.
Cap: deep flesh colour, varying to brownish, olivaceous lilac, or pinkish buff; at first hemispherical, becoming convex to flattened, often slightly depressed at disc; cuticle slightly viscid when damp, otherwise dull, glabrous, smooth, with slight radial striation, and characteristically falling short of cap margin in mature caps, by 1–2 mm.; margin may be slightly sulcate. Flesh off–white, firm, tinged cap colour immediately beneath cuticle.
Gills: white with rusty brown spotting when old; adnexed, thin shallow, crowded, ventricose, forked. Spores hyaline, white in the mass, spherical to piriform and weakly punctate 6–7 x 5–6 μ.
Stipe: white but typically rusty brown at base. Flesh white, firm, slightly brittle.
Odour: not distinctive. **Taste:** nutty.
Chemical tests: stipe deep flesh pink when rubbed with ferrous sulphate crystal; gills vivid lemon yellow with aniline.
Occurrence: common in some years, otherwise infrequent. August–November.

In spite of the unfortunate fact that this *Russula* is by no means common, it is worth keeping an eye open for it. It has certain quite distinctive characteristics, including the inter–mediate gills and the cuticle falling short of the cap margin. Furthermore, it makes very good eating.

RUSSULA VIOLEIPES Quél.

Habitat: mixed woods; solitary, or loosely scattered; on soil.
Dimensions: cap 4–8 cm. dia.; stipe 4–7 cm. tall x 1–2.5 cm. dia.
Cap: lemon yellow, or olive yellow, typically tinged violaceous or carmine; at first sub–spherical, becoming convex and finally plano–depressed; cuticle smooth, dry, shining, glabrous or minutely farinose, tending to be more white pruinose at disc in young specimens, margin slightly sulcate, and frequently cracked radially. Flesh white or pallid, at first solid, becoming more spongy.
Gills: at first white, then ivory yellow, occasionally with violaceous tinge; slightly decurrent, attenuated distally, narrow,

Russula vesca

greasy to touch. Spores hyaline, pale cream in the mass, sub–spherical, echinate with reticulations 6–9 x 6–8 μ.

Stipe: white or tinged lemon yellow, with violaceous or carmine flushing; ventricose or irregular, finely farinose or pruinose. Flesh white or pallid, at first firm and full, becoming spongy, cavernose.

Odour: at first fruity, but in older specimens, of fish (cf *R. xerampelina*).

Occurrence: not common. September–November.

RUSSULA VIRESCENS (Schaeff. ex Zant.) Fr.

Habitat: deciduous woods, favouring beech, also recorded under ccnifers; typically in open grassy clearings, edges of woods, firebreaks etc; solitary; on soil.

Dimensions: cap 6–14 cm. dia.; stipe 4–9 cm. tall x 2–4 cm. dia.

Cap: wholly verdigris green, with dull rust brown spots in older specimens; at first hemispherical, becoming convex to flattened, and slightly depressed at disc; cuticle coarsely farinose at first, the surface bearing small irregular squamules, finally the whole cuticle cracking into radially arranged squamules; margin may be slightly sulcate or striate. Flesh white, tending to become discoloured brown where it shows through cracks, firm, rather brittle.

Gills: white, becoming off–white or cream, adnexed or free, crowded, narrow, forked. Spores creamy or dirty white, more or less spherical, shortly echinate or punctate with reticulate venation 8–10 x 7–8 μ.

Stipe: white, spotted brown where damaged; at first pruinose, becoming wholly glabrous. Flesh white, at first firm, brittle, becoming spongy.

Odour: freshly cut surface faintly fruity, older specimens fishy.

Occurrence: fairly common. August–November.

R. virescens is an excellent fleshy fungus for the table, and I would well recommend it.

The Milanese peasants regard it as a great delicacy and traditionally toast it over wood embers on a griddle. If it is then eaten with a little seasoning, it has a delicious savoury smell and a taste reminiscent of shellfish.

The fungus is also good for drying but is reported to develop a strong smell in the process, so I would not recommend putting it in a drying cabinet with the laundry.

RUSSULA XERAMPELINA (Schaeff. ex Secr.) Fr.

   Habitat: mixed woods, generally gregarious, less often solitary; on soil.
   Dimensions: cap 5–12 cm. dia.; stipe 4–6 cm. tall x 1.5–3.0 cm. dia.
   Cap: wine colour with variation towards purple and brown tinges, may also be paler; at first convex becoming convex–expanded, slightly depressed at disc; cuticle at first viscid for brief period, then dry and minutely velvety, separable to ½ cap diameter, finely sulcate at the margin in older specimens. Flesh pallid or tinged lemon yellow.
   Gills: at first pallid, becoming more creamy–ochre, brown where bruised; free, rounded, broad and fragile. Spores hyaline, white in the mass, more or less spherical and coarsely echinate 8–13 μ.
   Stipe: off–white with variable amount of red tingeing, bruising dirty olive brown; pruinose with reticulate venation or generally rugose; slightly clavate. Flesh white, stuffed, spongy.
   Odour: strongly fishy in older specimens, otherwise vaguely fruity, or without distinctive smell.
   Chemical tests: stipe deep olive green when rubbed with ferrous sulphate crystal; gills coral red with aniline.
   Occurrence: common. August–November.

   This is one of a limited number of fungus species where the use of a simple chemical test is useful to aid positive identification, because a number of related species do tend to have similar colouring and if one is collecting young specimens, the characteristic lobstery smell is not noticeable; indeed, if it is, I strongly recommend leaving the specimen where you find it, because it will be past safe use in cooking.

TRICHOLOMA CINGULATUM (Almfelt apud Fr.) Jac.

   Habitat: typically confined to damp, boggy places, under willows; solitary, or gregarious; on soil.
   Dimensions: cap 5–7 cm. dia.; stipe 6–8 cm. tall x 1.0–1.5 cm. dia.
   Cap: at first pallid, becoming brownish grey, or ash, less typically tinged yellowish rufous; at first convex, becoming plano–convex or expanded umbonate, and finally depressed

Russula xerampe

with revolute margin; cuticle dry with adpressed floccose squamules superimposed on faintly fibrillose base. Flesh greyish white, becoming more dirty grey, thin.

Gills: off–white, adnate or free, emarginate, at first crowded, becoming more distant. Spores hyaline, white in the mass, ellipsoidal, smooth 6–8 x 3–4 μ.

Stipe: concolorous with gills, flexuose, slightly attenuated upwards, with distinct white, floccose annulus; stipe fibrillose below annulus. Flesh greyish white, more or less hollow, or loosely stuffed.

Odour: faintly farinose.

Occurrence: very localised. August–October.

The genus *Tricholoma* includes a number of largish, fleshy species, all of which are probably edible, although some have bitter or rancid flavours which make them unsuitable.

In the main, they are firm fleshed and can be used in a variety of ways. The best known is probably the vernal specie, *T. gambosum,* St. George's mushroom, but a number of others listed provide excellent medium flavours. The blewits used to be placed in the *Tricholoma* genus at one time, but it is now considered more correct to place them in the separate genus *Lepista*.

TRICHOLOMA COLUMBETTA (Fr.) Kümmer.

Habitat: light frondose woods, and edges of woods, favouring beech and oak; solitary or scattered; on soil.

Dimensions: cap 5–10 cm. dia.; stipe 5–10 cm. tall x 2.0–2.5 cm. dia.

Cap: wholly white, typically discolouring in old specimens with grey blue spots; at first convex, becoming plano–convex and finally plano–expanded with obtuse, slightly flexuose margin; cuticle at first minutely tomentose then shining silky fibrillose, or smooth, margin may be faintly squamulose. Flesh white, firm.

Gills: white, at first mildly sinuate then almost free, broad, emarginate. Spores hyaline, white in the mass, ovate, smooth, 6–8 x 3–4 μ.

Stipe: white, stoutish, fibrillose, rooting. Flesh white, firm, full.

Odour: not distinctive.

Occurrence: occasional. August–November.

133

TRICHOLOMA FLAVOVIRENS (Pers. ex Fr.) Lund.

Habitat: coniferous woods, favouring pine; solitary, on soil.
Dimensions: cap 7–12 cm. dia.; stipe 4–8 cm. tall x 2.0–3.5 cm. dia.
Cap: basically greenish yellow, or olive yellow, tending to become greener with age, slightly rufescent towards disc; at first convex, becoming plano–expanded with involute margin, and finally broadly flexuose with obtuse margin; cuticle smooth, glabrous, viscid, squamulose at the disc. Flesh off–white, thick, firm.
Gills: at first off–white, becoming pale yellow, and finally sulphur yellow; scarcely adnexed, ventricose, emarginate, broad, and crowded. Spores hyaline, white in the mass, ellipsoidal, smooth, 6–8 x 3.5–4.5 μ.
Stipe: pale sulphur yellow, stout, fibrillose or minutely squamulose. Flesh white, full, firm.
Odour: faintly farinose.
Occurrence: not infrequent. August–October.

TRICHOLOMA GAMBOSUM (Fr.) Kümmer. St. George's mushroom.

Habitat: grassy clearings, edges of frondose woods etc, favouring calcareous soils; solitary; on soil.
Dimensions: cap 6–12 cm. dia.; stipe 4–10 cm. tall x 2.0–4.5 cm. dia.
Cap: off–white or cream colour, ageing more ochraceous or pale alutaceous, more pallid when dry; at first campanulate–convex, soon becoming expanded and typically flexuose, with part involute and part revolute margin, may become slightly depressed with age; cuticle at first tomentose at the margin, soon becoming wholly smooth, glabrous, typically somewhat shining when dry, dull when wet, may become cracked with age. Flesh white, brittle, thick.
Gills: at first white, slowly becoming pallid cream with greyish tinge, typically sinuate, may also be adnate or slightly decurrent, thin, crowded, brittle. Spores hyaline, white in the mass, ovate, smooth, 5–7 x 3–4.5 μ.
Stipe: concolorous with cap, slightly floccose above, tomentose at base, fibrillose. Flesh white, fibrillar, full, massive.
Odour: farinose. **Taste:** farinose.
Occurrence: occasional. April–May.

There seems to be some controversy about the best method of cooking this fungus. A Government bulletin, published by H.M.S.O. in 1947, specifically does not recommend stewing. However, the general concensus of opinion on the Continent, in addition to sautéing, seems to favour cooking in wine or stock.

My own experience of the fungus is limited, because I never seem to find the time to do much strenuous fungus hunting during the spring months. I cannot, therefore, advocate one method or the other on grounds of personal experience.

TRICHOLOMA PORTENTOSUM (Fr.) Quél..Dingy agaric.

Habitat: coniferous and frondose woods, favouring pine; often loosely gregarious; on sandy soil.

Dimensions: cap 5–10 cm. dia.; stipe 5–10 cm. tall x 1.5–3.0 cm. dia.

Cap: smokey grey, tinged with brown or violet, almost black at disc, with radiating, black, fibrillose striations; cuticle typically cracking radially from disc in older specimens, almost wholly detachable, glabrous, and more or less dry to the touch; at first convex, becoming irregularly expanded. Flesh white, but pigmented greyish immediately under cuticle, thin.

Gills: at first white, becoming tinged yellowish or dirty grey; sinuate, slightly ventricose, thickened basally. Spores hyaline, white in the mass, briefly ellipsoidal, smooth, 6–7 x 4–5 μ.

Stipe: white or tinged yellowish, or greyish, glabrous, stout; Flesh off–white, full, fibrillar, medium.

Odour: farinose. **Taste:** farinose.

Occurrence: infrequent, though probably more common in specific localities. September–October.

There seems to be little specific information available concerning this fungus, though I have established that at one time or another it had achieved great popularity in Bohemia where in certain parts it could frequently be seen displayed for sale in open markets.

Pilât recommends peeling the cap, I suspect because it is somewhat fibrillar.

It is one of those specimens which is probably worth collecting if you find a large group of them and nothing more exciting is at hand. It is fairly easily recognisable by the radiating fibrils on the cap, and the stout stem makes up for the rather thin flesh in the cap. As far as I know there are no particular recipes for cooking it.

136   *Tricholoma portento.*

BOLETUS BADIUS Fr.

Habitat: coniferous woods, particularly favouring pine, and western red cedar; solitary; on soil.

Dimensions: cap 4–12 cm. dia.; stipe 4–10 cm. tall x 1–4 cm. dia.

Cap: bay brown or chestnut (sub–species are now recognised having colour variations through reddish brown, and dense bay brown, verging on black); at first more or less hemispherical, becoming convex to plane, often with slightly revolute margin on old specimens; cuticle at first tomentose, becoming wholly glabrous, always viscid in wet weather. Flesh off–white, slightly brownish beneath cuticle, firm, becoming slightly yellow and softer with age; can turn very slightly blue where bruised, in older specimens.

Pores: at first pallid, becoming pale yellow, or greenish yellow, bruising bluish green. Tubes concolorous with pores, free, minute, round. Spores pale yellow, olive brown in the mass, fusiform, smooth, 12–15 x 4–5 μ.

Stipe: pale olive yellow, turning blue where bruised, tan beneath cap, and whitish tomentose at base; irregularly fibrillose–striate. Flesh firm at first, becoming softer with age, weakly fibrillar.

Odour: not distinctive.

Occurrence: common. September–November.

With remarkably few exceptions, the *Boletus* genus provide excellent material for the table. Those members to be avoided are not considered to be dangerously poisonous and are unsuitable on account of extremely bitter taste.

It is not necessary to remove pores nor to peel the skin, unless it is specifically recommended, but I would advocate cooking these fungi rather than using them raw. All tend to be rather spongy in texture, and for salads crisp–fleshed specimens are more desirable. However, they are full of juice and flavour when cooked, as well as being pleasantly tender.

One essential precaution is to collect the fungi young and fresh. I have reiterated this advice in other places, but Boletae in particular very quickly becomes worm–ridden in warm weather. Look carefully for signs of bore holes when picking.

BOLETUS BOVINUS L. ex Fr.

Habitat: coniferous woods, favouring pine, and sandy soils; solitary; on soil.

Dimensions: cap 4–9 cm. dia.; stipe 2–8 cm. tall x 0.5–2.0 cm. dia.

Cap: pale yellowish brown to reddish buff, often with pink tinge, darker towards disc; at first plano–convex and somewhat involute at the margin, becoming irregularly expanded; cuticle slightly tomentose at the margin when young, becoming wholly viscid, shining, separable in fragments. Flesh yellowish brown, pallid, unchanging or very slightly blue where cut, rubbery elastic at first, becoming soft and spongy, thick.

Pores: at first pale yellowish, becoming finally more or less olive brown, unchanging. Tubes concolorous with pores, adnate–decurrent, short, compound (surface pores dividing into smaller tubes below). Spores pale yellow, ellipsoid–fusiform, smooth, 6–10 x 3–4 μ.

Stipe: slightly paler than cap cuticle, slightly tomentose–floccose at the base, otherwise finely fibrillose. Attenuated downwards. Flesh yellowish, unchanging or very slightly blue where cut, slightly fibrillar.

Odour: not distinctive.

Occurrence: fairly common. July–November.

BOLETUS CRYSENTERON (Bull. ex St. Amans)

Habitat: typically in frondose woods; solitary; on soil.

Dimensions: cap 4–10 cm. dia.; stipe 4–8 cm. tall x 1.0–2.5 cm. dia.

Cap: reddish brown, often tinged yellowish to olive green; at first hemispherical, becoming convex to pulvinate; cuticle minutely tomentose, as a faint 'bloom', later cracking and showing red flesh beneath. Flesh red beneath cap cuticle, otherwise yellowish, becoming reddish in older specimens; soft, thick.

Pores: at first pale yellow, becoming dirty olive. Tubes concolorous with pores, almost free, long, minute, round. Spores yellowish olive, ellipsoidal, smooth, 11–15 x 4–5 μ.

Stipe: yellowish, typically whitish tomentose at base. Flesh yellowish, thick.

Odour: not distinctive.

Occurrence: common. August–November.

139   *Boletus bovinus*

140   Boletus crysen.

BOLETUS EDULIS Bull. ex.Fr. Cep.

Habitat: fairly open frondose woods, and clearings, also in hedgerows, particularly under beech and oak; solitary; on soil.

Dimensions: cap 5–20 cm. dia.; stipe 5–15 cm. tall x 2–4 cm. dia.

Cap: light to mid–brown; at first hemispherical, becoming convex to pulvinate; cuticle slightly tomentose in dry weather, more or less viscid when moist. Flesh white, brownish beneath cuticle, otherwise unchanging, firm, thick.

Pores: at first off–white, becoming tinged yellowish grey. Tubes concolorous with pores, almost free, long, minute, round. Spores yellowish olive, ellipsoidal, smooth, 14–17 x 4–5 μ.

Stipe: more or less concolorous with cap, though lighter; swollen clavate, with distinctive network of white, raised veins, more prominent towards apex.

Odour: not distinctive.

Occurrence: occasional to frequent. August–October.

Worthington Smith describes this fungus as proving 'one of the most delicious and tender objects of food ever submitted to the operation of cooking'. On this occasion I am inclined to agree with him, for the cep is undoubtedly a highly 'more–ish' delicacy.

Collect it young and very fresh; older specimens tend to become very wormy and soggy in texture. It is not necessary to peel it or to remove the tubes, though some people may prefer to do so.

The recipes for cooking ceps are numerous, and this is one of the toadstools that has achieved great commercial popularity in the British Isles. It used to be a common sight on the market stalls at Covent Garden and is apparently still available in dried form in certain London delicatessens.

One of the old Victorian recipes for the fungus was to bake it in a closed casserole pot, with onions and butter, but it is suitable for practically any sort of experiment, either as a dish in itself, or to add relish to other dishes, or to dry and store.

On the Continent it has been a popular dish since Roman times. They were not the 'boleti' of the Romans, but enjoyed the popular name of 'suilli', on account of the curious fact that Italian pigs seem to relish them. They are still described in Italian recipe books by this name.

In the days of the Roman Empire, 'suilli' would have been prepared by stewing in stock with liquamen and pounded pepper. Alternatively, they were served uncooked with a dressing of pepper, vinegar, oil and 'caroenum'.

Today Italian recipes generally substitute oil for the liquamen. The stalks are cut off and the caps laid upside down. Salt and

141

pepper are liberally applied to the porous surface, followed by melted butter or oil. The caps are baked in the oven, turning once, until tender.

Elsewhere in Europe, the popularity of *Boletus* has spread far and wide, probably aided by the ramifications of the Roman Empire. Italy, Czechoslovakia, Russia, Germany and Poland, have all exported the fungi commercially at one time or another, and their popularity has extended as far as Scandinavia. Much of the popularity must be attributed to the fact that apart from being temptingly fleshy, very few of the *Boletus* group are even mildly poisonous, and because of the substitution of pores for gills there is little chance of their being mistaken for more unpleasant relatives.

Young *Boletus edulis* is excellent when added raw to a salad.

In Hungary, a traditional soup is made from dried *Boletus*. The caps are soaked in warm water and toasted bread is added till the whole takes on the consistency of a purée. This is rubbed through a sieve. A number of stewed whole caps are added, and the mixture is boiled together, and served with salt and pepper.

All in all an extremely versatile fungus and excellent material for experiment in the kitchen. Only a very limited number of pore–bearing fungi are even mildly poisonous, and then only because of intensely bitter or peppery taste, so you are very unlikely to make a serious mistake in collection. In the following pages, I have detailed a number of *Boletus* species which make equally excellent eating, and in the poisonous section the types which have unpleasant taste are to be found.

If I were advocating any particular type of fungus for a beginner, I think I would go for any of these species as a priority.

On a very different point of interest, *Boletus edulis* is sus– pected to have beneficial properties in the retardation of certain types of cancer. An American worker, E. H. Lucas from the Michigan Academy of Science, who is an expert on folklore and plant drugs, visited a tiny village in the mountains of Bohemia, close to the Bavarian border, during the 1930s. There he learnt of an old folklore apparently relating to *B. edulis*. Lumberjacks working in the area had implicit faith in the idea that eating the fungus prevented cancer.

When Lucas returned to the United States, the idea was tried out using a cancer bred in laboratory mice, called mouse sarcoma 180, at the Sloan Kettering Institute for Cancer Research. The result was a remarkable demonstration of cancer inhibition. Unfortunately the further application of such medication has since been rendered impractical, because *B. edulis* cannot be effectively grown in cultivation. The active chemicals found in its tissues thought to be responsible for the cancer retardation, are extremely complex and cannot readily be synthesised.

These curious properties are reflected in another edible fungus, *Calvatia gigantea,* the giant puffball, which is referred to in detail on page 154.

Boletus edulis

BOLETUS ELEGANS Schum. ex Fr.

Habitat: under larches only; typically loosely gregarious, but never caespitose; on soil.
Dimensions: cap 4–14 cm. dia.; stipe 4–10 cm. tall x 1.0–2.5 cm. dia.
Cap: light golden yellow, or orange yellow; at first sub–spherical, becoming convex to flattened, typically with slight, blunt umbo; cuticle very viscid. Flesh lemon yellow, becoming dirty grey with slight pink or lilac tinge where cut; soft, spongy, rather watery medium.
Pores: at first covered by yellowish fugacious veil, leaving annulus on stipe; pores lemon yellow or olive yellow bruising pinkish brown. Tubes concolorous with pores, adnate, short, smallish, round. Spores very pale yellow, deeper yellow in the mass, ellipsoidal, smooth 7–10 x 3–4 μ.
Stipe: golden yellow above annulus, typically with slight reticulate sculpturing; annulus whitish yellow, membraneous; below annulus more brownish yellow, tomentose, punctate to fibrillose. Flesh lemon yellow but more fibrillar than in cap.
Odour: not distinctive.
Occurrence: (May) June–September (Oct).

BOLETUS ERYTHROPUS (Fr. ex Fr.) Secr.

Habitat: mixed woods favouring beech, less common under fire and spruce; solitary, or in small groups; on soil.
Dimensions: cap 5–20 cm. dia.; stipe 5–15 cm. tall x 2–4 cm. dia.
Cap: dark brown with russet or yellowish tinge in some specimens; at first hemispherical then pulvinate–expanded; cuticle minutely tomentose or velvety, never viscid, turning more or less black where bruised and becoming very dark when old. Flesh yellow and firm, juicy; immediately turning dark blue where cut.
Pores: at first yellowish or greenish yellow, becoming crimson when mature, and later paling somewhat in old speci–mens, bruising dark blue at all stages. Tubes yellowish green, sinuate, small in diameter, rounded in cross section, long; immediately turning blue when cut. Spores olive yellow, dirty olive green in the mass, fusiform, smooth 13–18 x 5–7 μ.
Stipe: yellow under cap, otherwise red tomentose, punctate; at first ventricose, becoming massively clavate with elongation. Flesh yellow, immediately turning blue where cut, firm, juicy, thick.
Odour: not distinctive.
Occurrence: fairly frequent. August–November.

144

Boletus elegans

BOLETUS GRANULATUS L. ex Fr.

Habitat: coniferous woods, favouring pine, typically in open grassy clearings, firebreaks, edges of woods etc; solitary; on soil.

Dimensions: cap 4–10 cm. dia.; stipe 4–6 cm. tall x 1.0–1.5 cm. dia.

Cap: at first rusty yellow, becoming more ochre yellow; at first convex with involute margin, becoming expanded and slightly irregular with more or less revolute margin; cuticle viscid, glabrous, somewhat silky in dry weather, easily separable from cap. Flesh yellowish, unchanging, at first firm, becoming spongy, thick.

Pores: dirty yellow to olive yellow, unchanging. Tubes concolorous with pores, adnexed, minute, round, oozing whitish latex in young sporophore, which encrusts as small, white granules on pores, and stipe apex. Spores pale yellow, deeper yellow in the mass, fusiform, smooth, 8–10 x 2–3 μ.

Stipe: short relative to cap diameter, quite slender, pale yellow, but whiter and somewhat granular at apex. Flesh pale yellow, full.

Odour: reminiscent of butter according to some authorities. Similar in taste.

Occurrence: fairly frequent. August–November.

BOLETUS LUTEUS L. ex Fr.

Habitat: near conifers, favouring pine, typically in open grassy clearings, edges of woods, firebreaks etc; solitary; on soil.

Dimensions: cap 4–10 cm. dia.; stipe 4–10 cm. tall x 1.5–2.5 cm. dia.

Cap: yellowish brown to orange brown, may have slight brownish purple tinge at margin (remnant of veil); at first hemispherical, becoming convex to plane, typically with involute margin, and slight blunt umbo; cuticle very viscid, and radially fibrillose striate, more apparent when dry, completely separable. Flesh whitish yellow, deeper yellow adjacent to pores, unchanging, spongy, rather watery, medium.

Pores: lemon yellow, becoming more olive yellow; at first covered by white coriaceous veil, soon fugacious, leaving brownish purple fragments adhering to cap margin, and as an annulus on the stipe. Tubes concolorous with pores, adnexed, becoming partly compressed when old, easily separable from cap, quite long, smallish in diameter, angular. Spores pale yellow, more lemon yellow in the mass, ellipsoidal, smooth, 7–10 x 3–5 μ.

Stipe: bearing obvious brownish purple annulus; pale lemon

above annulus, and viscid, granular; more brownish or greyish yellow below. Flesh whitish yellow, unchanging, fibrillar, medium.
Odour: not distinctive.
Occurrence: fairly common. August–November.

This should be a fairly easy specimen to identify, since it is the only British *Boletus* with a dark–coloured annulus.

It is popular in certain parts of Europe as one of the better members of the family for eating, though it is unsuitable for drying, since it deteriorates too rapidly.

Don't be put off by the slimy texture of the cap. This can be peeled off. In any case the viscose part completely disappears when the fungus is cooked in a soup or stew. You may find it too glutinous merely fried or baked by itself.

The best way of storing the caps is to peel and pickle them.

BOLETUS PIPERATUS (IXOCOMUS) *Bull. ex Fr. *Quél.

Habitat: coniferous woods, favouring sandy soils; solitary or in small groups; on soil.
Dimensions: cap 2–6 cm. dia.; stipe 3–6 cm. tall x 0.5–1.5 cm. dia.
Cap: yellowish brown, to pale cinnamon; at first hemispherical becoming convex, and finally plano–convex; cuticle smooth, glabrous when dry, viscid in damp weather. Flesh yellowish, soft, unchanging, thick.
Pores: reddish brown, unchanging. Tubes fulvous to cinnamon, unchanging, adnate or slightly decurrent, large, angular. Spores fusiform, pale yellow, smooth $10–14 \times 3–4\,\mu$.
Stipe: yellowish brown, to cinnamon, bright yellow at the base, unchanging, smooth, relatively thin. Flesh yellowish, unchanging, soft, full.
Odour: not distinctive. **Taste:** very peppery.
Occurrence: not common. August–October.

BOLETUS VARIEGATUS L. ex Fr.

Habitat: coniferous woods and sandy heaths, favouring pines; typically scattered extensively; on soil.
Dimensions: cap 5–12 cm. dia.; stipe 4–8 cm. tall x 1.0–2.5 cm. dia.

Cap: dull ochre or yellowish brown, covered with small closely adpressed, soft, darker scales; at first convex, becoming irregularly expanded; cuticle very viscid in damp weather. Flesh yellowish, bluish where bruised or cut; tenaceous, firm.

Pores: at first pale yellow, becoming more olive brown or olive yellow, bluish where bruised. Tubes concolorous with pores, blue where cut, adnexed, fairly small. Spores ochre, more olivaceous in the mass, fusiform, smooth, $11-14 \times 5-6\,\mu$.

Stipe: yellowish brown above, darker brown below, stout, smooth. Flesh concolorous with cap, turning bluish where cut, tinged reddish at the base, firm.

Odour: not distinctive.

Occurrence: common. August–November.

BOLETUS SCABER Bull. ex Fr.

Habitat: typically under birch, but may be found under hornbeam; solitary or loosely scattered; on soil.

Dimensions: cap 5–18 cm. dia.; stipe 5–15 cm. tall x 1–4 cm. dia.

Cap: grey brown to smokey brown; at first hemispherical, becoming irregularly convex–expanded, rugose; cuticle at first tomentose, soon wholly glabrous, often irregularly cracked, and darker where bruised. Never viscid. Flesh dirty white to buff, or slightly yellowish pink, turning faint greyish violet where cut, firm, thick.

Pores: off-white at first, becoming dirty buff, darker violet grey where bruised. Tubes concolorous with pores, free, minute, round. Spores yellowish brown, dirty brown in the mass, fusiform, smooth $10-18 \times 5-6\,\mu$.

Stipe: off–white background with black, striate, scurfy markings; more or less rugose under cap, and sub–ventricose below, firm, medium.

Odour: not distinctive.

Occurrence: common. August–October.

One amusing attribute both of this fungus and the related *B. edulis* is that cattle have been known to become addicted to eating it, an unusual feature amongst mammalian herbivores. It enjoys the popular title of cow fungus in Norway.

Some authorities advocate removing the pores before cooking, but unless they are particularly dirty this is quite unnecessary.

B. scaber is extremely common, and makes an excellent meal, either stewed or sautéed.

149   *Boletus variegatus*

Boletus sca

151   *Boletus scaber* (showing colour variation)

†BOLETUS TESTACEOSCABER Secr.

Habitat: typically under birch, but also occasionally in mixed woods; prefers open woodland or fringes of woods; solitary; on soil.

Dimensions: cap 5–20 cm. dia.; stipe 5–15 cm. tall x 2–4 cm. dia.

Cap: typically reddish orange, but may be more yellowish; at first hemispherical, becoming convex; cuticle finely tomentose, dry, never viscid; at first bearing appendicular remains of pellicle at the margin, adpressed to stipe when young. Flesh white, very slowly turning pale lilac or slate on exposure to air, firm, thick.

Pores: at first off–white, becoming pale greyish brown. Tubes concolorous with pores, free, minute, round. Spores yellowish, more brown in the mass, fusiform, smooth, 12–16 x 4–5 μ.

Odour: not distinctive.

Occurrence: frequent but not common. August–November.

GYROPORUS CYANESCENS (BOLETUS) (Bull. ex Fr.) Quél.

Habitat: typically in coniferous woods, favouring spruce; solitary; on soil.

Dimensions: cap 5–12 cm. dia.; stipe 5–10 cm. tall x 2.0–2.5 cm. dia.

Cap: yellowish cream or with slight green tinge, covered with closely adpressed pale brown squamules; at first sub–spherical, becoming irregularly convex; cuticle dry. Flesh off–white, becoming blue violet or indigo where cut; firm.

Pores: at first pallid, becoming yellowish cream, bruising indigo; tubes concolorous with pores, free, minute, rounded. Spores pale yellow, ellipsoidal, smooth 8–10 x 5–6 μ.

Stipe: yellowish cream, pallid under cap; smooth, minutely velvety, at first ventricose, becoming sub–cylindrical or clavate, attenuated upwards. Flesh off–white, turning blue violet or indigo where cut; deeply cavernose, hard, fragile.

Odour: not distinctive.

Occurrence: very infrequent. August–October.

---

†The naming of this fungus and several related species, is likely to cause some confusion, because a number of very similar variations are now listed.

Boletus testaceoscaber

CALVATIA GIGANTEA (LYCOPERDON) *Schaeff. *Pers.
Giant puffball.

Habitat: variable—open pastures, fringes of woods, gardens, mossy banks etc; solitary; on soil.
Dimensions: sporophore 15–40 cm. dia.
Sporophore: globose, sessile, consisting of thick, coriaceous peridium enclosing inner spore forming gleba. Peridium white to cream colour, smooth, glabrous, slightly sulcate at sterile pedestal; becoming greenish as spores mature, peridium finally breaking away in the upper region to release spores. Gleba at first pure white, later becoming yellowish or greenish as spores ripen, and finally black. Spores olive brown, almost black in the mass, spherical, verrucose, 4–5 μ.
Odour: not distinctive.
Occurrence: not infrequent but localised.

A veritable eye–goggler of a fungus when fully grown, some specimens reach a size considerably larger than a football and when ripe discharge literally millions of spores, like the mouth of some rustic blast furnace.

The giant puffballs are, alas, rather a rarity, perhaps sur–prisingly considering the potential numbers of their offspring.

However, the human population tend to regard them as unwholesome freaks which should be destroyed on sight. Many end their days as footballs, and I imagine that few manage to reach maturity for these reasons.

Whilst engaged on compiling this section, I happened to mention giant puffball to a friend. He recalled an incident whilst on holiday some years ago when he had come across one of these splendid specimens. Knowing something of their culinary worth, he had been enthusiastic about the prospects of a puffball banquet, but so horrified were his companions that they insisted on destroying the specimen before my friend could do himself any permanent damage. Apparently they felt him to be in the grip of powerful forces, and the temptation must be thoroughly removed lest he secret the strange object away to some clandestine orgy of his own.

Enough levity, but the illustration does serve the point that as a race, we are strongly reticent about sampling the unknown, particularly where our stomachs are concerned. A great pity, because this is one of those fungi which offer a real treat for the more stout–hearted.

Although nowadays the giant puffball is valued only by an enlightened few, in bygone times it was held in higher regard. In her excellent book *Food in England,* Dorothy Hartley details a number of charming old English recipes for puffballs.

155   *Calvatia gigantea* (young sporophore)

Traditionally, the giant puffball is cut into slices like a loaf of bread (incidentally, it must be pure white all the way through). The slices are dipped into beaten egg, and then coated with breadcrumbs. It is recommended that the crumbs be pressed firmly in, and the slices left for a few hours. The coated slices are then fried on both sides, seasoned and served hot.

It is quite unnecessary to peel the specimens unless the outer skin is dirty.

The texture is deliciously crumbly, and the dish is considered by some to be reminiscent of sweetbreads.

Another suggestion is to hollow out the whole puffball, chop the centre part finely and mix with sage—and—onion stuffing. This mixture is returned to the shell and draped with back bacon. The whole can then conveniently be wrapped in foil and baked in the oven at 325°F for one hour.

Puffballs, incidentally, were a novelty favourite at the Free—masons Tavern in London in past days, when they appeared on the menu for State occasions.

I have made mention of the fact that extract from the agaric fungus *Boletus edulis* has the apparent effect of retarding certain types of cancer. It is now suspected that certain other types of fungi have similar inhibitory action. One of those which has received considerable scientific attention is *Calvatia gigantea.*

Experimental projects at the Sloan Kettering Institute for Cancer Research were directed towards finding a suitable fungus whose sporophores could be grown under controlled conditions. In the case of *Boletus edulis,* no satisfactory method of inducing sporophore production has yet been devised. However, the basidiospores of several *Calvatia* spp. have now been successfully germinated.

The main drawback as yet to any real progress in this field is the enormous amount of raw material needed to extract the pharmacological principle—calvacin. In this case, 1,500 lbs. of puffballs will yield approximately 1 lb. calvacin. Furthermore, only the young immature sporophores appear to be effective in the inhibitory action.

A further problem is that after extensive use, calvacin appears to give rise to allergic side—effects in mammals.

LYCOPERDON PERLATUM Pers. Devil's tobacco pouch.
LYCOPERDON GEMMATUM Batsch.

Habitat: woods generally, but more common under conifers; solitary, gregarious, or caespitose; on soil.
Dimensions: sporophore 3–5 cm. dia.; 4–8 cm. tall.
Sporophore: clavate or piriform, typically umbonate at first.

Lycoperdon perlatum

Consisting of peridium surrounding fertile gleba. Peridium at first pure white, becoming slightly yellow or green, finally greyish brown; consisting of outer exoperidium at first bearing short, pointed, fugacious warts, surrounded by coarse, mealy granules, and an inner endoperidium at first fragile and membraneous, later becoming more coriaceous, and finally papery, opening at the apex by a small, single pore; pallid scars remain where the warts fall off; pedestal lacks warts and is attached to the substratum by obvious white mycelial strands. Gleba at first pure white and fairly firm, becoming more spongy and greenish yellow, finally powdery and olive brown with ripe spore mass, which is intermingled with fine threads—the capillitium.

Spores: olive brown, weakly echinate, spherical, 3–4 μ.

Odour: not distinctive.

Occurrence: common and widespread. August–November.

The quaint popular name of this puffball stems, I think, from Central Europe. When the gleba is ripe, the spores can be observed puffing out in dark satanic–looking clouds, hence the allusion! The specimens are much sought after as a poor man's sweetbread, and of all the alleged similarities to meat dishes in the fungal realm, this is one of the more realistic analogies. The texture is not unlike that of a sweetbread and the flavour is distinctly reminiscent.

Providing that the fruit bodies are really white all the way through and are used on the day of picking, the taste is extremely good and well worth trying.

The traditional European way of cooking is to cut into slices, dust with flour, turn lightly in beaten egg yolk, and finally coat with breadcrumbs. The resulting cutlets should be sautéed in butter for about five minutes. I suspect that most of the specimens to be collected are really too small to make the recipe anything but fiddly, and a more practical alternative is to put the whole specimens through the flour, egg, and breadcrumb process, without slicing them up.

A further alternative is to stew gently in milk until tender, and make a white sauce from the resultant juice. I would add the juice of half a lemon, too.

SCLERODERMA AURANTIUM L. ex Pers. Common earthball.

Habitat: woods and heaths generally, though not under dense tree cover; preferring sandy or peaty soils, often among moss or heather.

159   *Scleroderma aurantium*

Dimensions: sporophore 3–10 cm. dia.

Sporophore: tuberous, sessile, consisting of thick coriaceous peridium, enclosing inner spore forming gleba. Peridium at first yellowish to dirty white and fairly smooth, later becoming greenish and cracked into scales or warts, finally breaking open to release ripe spore mass. Gleba at first pure white, slowly turning pale pink where cut; later as spores ripen, becoming yellowish or greenish, and finally dense black, tinged with purple. Spores black, verrucose or reticulate, spherical, 7–12 μ.

Odour: not distinctive.

Occurrence: prolific and widespread, July–January; old fruit bodies persisting through winter.

An unlikely inclusion, you may think, until you discover that in Prague and other eastern European capitals the humble earthball finds its way into the most exclusive restaurants!

In any quantity, *Scleroderma* is poisonous, causing sickness and even unconsciousness, but used with discretion, it lends a delightfully aromatic flavour to a dish, not unlike that of truffles. It is even incorporated into a cheap ersatz truffle sausage that is much sought after, rivalling the British banger.

I have never come across the use of this fungus in England, but perhaps it could start a new trend in British sausage making.

AURICULARIA AURICULA Hook. 'Jew's ear'.

Habitat: typically on elder, very rarely on other frondose trees; solitary or gregarious to caespitose, occasionally imbricate.

Dimensions: 5–10 cm. dia. (1–2 mm. thick).

Sporophore: typically liver brown, but may be pallid or rosy. Varying from ear shaped to irregular, generally resupinate–reflexed, but may be sub–stipitate. Rubbery–gelatinous when moist; horny and brittle when dry; can be almost translucent. Upper (outer) cuticle pilose; inner surface bearing hymenium glabrous, with ventriculose folds. Spores fusiform, smooth, 16–20 x 5–9 μ.

Occurrence: common, September–December; but can be found throughout the year.

Although most authorities hasten to describe this fungus in glowing terms with regard to its culinary value, few seem keen to offer any bright ideas about cooking it.

Before entering into any discussion about cooking *Auricularia* it is as well to bear in mind that the fungus is a member of the

161

Tremellales, or jelly fungus group. As such, it can withstand considerable desiccation when it dries out to a bone-hard, black lump. However, with resumption of damp or rainy weather, it regenerates to its normal soft, brownish grey, almost translucent appearance. For this reason, it is only advisable to collect the fungus in damp or wet weather.

The fungus is usually quite firmly attached to the elder bark. Use a sharp knife for removal to avoid tearing the flesh.

The caps basically are tough and rubbery· any attempt to fry or sauté will result in something quite inedible, as we discovered. The best way of preparing the fungus would seem to be slow and careful cooking, by stewing in milk or stock in a closed casserole in the oven. I would recommend about three hours at a gentle heat. The texture when cooked in this way, is crisp, but finely flavoured and extremely palatable. If you are partial to Chinese food, the fungus makes an excellent vegetable dish. In fact a similar variety is grown commercially in China, on wooden palings.

CHAPTER FOUR

Fungal Poisons

Nature has far more brutal laws than we have come to accept in our world veneered with civilisation. Danger and death are matters of everyday life in the wild, and if one ventures into such an alien world one must be prepared to accept the rules. Most people in this country today, whether they like the idea or not, are well and truly urbanised—born and bred within some sort of conurbation—and the countryside is as unfamiliar as the local High Street would be to a deer or rabbit.

Thus, dabbling in the pastime of fungus eating must be treated with caution, and above all, good sense. The safe and simple rule is never eat anything unless you are quite positive of its identity and are sure that it falls into a safe category. The descriptions in a text book must never be considered a free pass–port to eating fungi. There is only one really safe way to identify in the field and that is to go out collecting with an expert, using reference books as a guide thereafter.

Many of the deaths which have resulted from eating poisonous fungi could have been avoided had the collector not imagined that they were well known edible varieties. *Amanita phalloides* has not infrequently lured people to their death, because they confused it with the field mushroom.

Having made my point, I would offer a more encouraging note to put the whole question of poisonous fungi into perspective. If one categorises fungi on a basis of edibility, then the poisonous species constitute by far and away the smallest group, and in this country, specimens like *A. phalloides* are decidedly uncommon in most seasons.

Types of fungal toxin

Poisonous fungi can be separated into a number of fairly distinct categories, based on their pharmacological action, but viewing them generally on a scale of effect, one finds other more obvious groupings.

At one end of the scale is the marginal group of edible fungi, which cause indigestion in allergic individuals, whilst at the other one finds extreme forms, whose toxins are lethal unless specific therapeutic measures are taken to counter their effects.

However, within these two extremes lie quite a number of species that cause symptoms which are not fatal under normal circumstances, but which can range from acute distress to the mild discomfort of a tummy ache.

There is also the fact that certain poisonous chemicals synthesised by fungi are thermolabile. In other words, their physiological action takes place if they are eaten raw, or partly cooked, but the action of heat converts them to other compounds which do not invoke the same harmful reaction. A number of fungi of this type are considered as delicacies on the Continent, even though in the raw state they would undoubtedly produce most unpleasant results.

Seven categories of pharmacological activity are recognised in Higher Fungi.

1. *Non–specific gastrointestinal toxins.*

A number of fungi synthesise substances which undoubtedly produce adverse physiological effects but which are not readily identifiable.

Perhaps the most important in this category is *Entoloma sinnuatum,* the effect of which is described, albeit in rather graphic terms, on page 200. One to two hours after eating, the subject experiences excruciating stomach pains, which are followed by violent and repeated vomiting. This sickness, in conjunction with profuse sweating and diarrhoea, typically can continue for as long as a week, and although the poison is not in itself lethal, the purgation may so weaken the patient as to cause death from exhaustion. However, this is unusual, and where fatalities have been reported, the victim has invariably been in poor health prior to eating the fungus.

A variety of other species—including *Agaricus xanthoderma, Russula emetica, Boletus satanas* and *Amanita rubescens,* to name some of the more common varieties—synthesise less virulent toxins which can have similar, if milder effects. Individual response to these can, however, vary considerably, and many of them are destroyed on cooking.

2. *Helvellic acid poisoning.*

Helvellic acid is synthesised by a number of Ascomycetes,

particularly *Gyromitra* species, and to a lesser extent the *Helvella* and *Morchella* fungi.

Its physiological action is haemolytic, breaking down red blood cells, and it gives rise to the conditions of haemoglobinurea and haemolytic jaundice. However, although violently toxic in the raw state, it is unstable when heated or if the fungus is dried out. Therefore, normal cooking processes technically render the fungus safe.

There are unfortunately some curious and, as yet, baffling anomalies. Take the case of a Canadian family, whose tragic misadventure with *Gyromitra esculenta* was widely reported some years ago. The mother, father, and a son aged sixteen collected clean, healthy–looking specimens of the fungus, soaked them in salt water overnight, and cooked and ate them for lunch on the following day. They had done this on innumerable occasions before without any ill effect, as *Gyromitra* is frequently eaten in certain parts of the world and is considered quite a delicacy, subject, of course, to its being adequately cooked.

However, somewhere between two and twelve hours after eating, all three experienced severe vomiting, abdominal pains, and diarrhoea mixed with blood. The parents, who had eaten only a small quantity of the fungus, recovered after a short while, but the son's condition deteriorated rapidly with the onset of delirium and convulsions. He died after forty–eight hours in deep coma, and post–mortem examination showed severe swelling of the liver with further damage to the kidneys and the appearance of marked jaundice.

Why this disaster should have happened when the subjects had previously eaten the fungus with complete immunity is unclear. Various theories have been put forward, the least convincing of which is the universal standby that there are two identical species, one of which is poisonous and the other edible. I think that this idea is not really to be regarded seriously, however.

Another, and perhaps more plausible, suggestion is that *Gyromitra* synthesises helvellic acid, but that this, or some other substances in its tissues, are converted with age to thermostable toxins. It is well known that fungi produce strongly toxic degradation products. If some of the specimens were 'border–line', the overnight soaking could have been just sufficient to produce other dangerous and more resistant substances.

3. *Mycoatropine poisoning.*

The toxin is synthesised by two species of *Amanita* — *A. muscaria* (fly agaric) and *A. pantherina* (panther cap) — and is known to have pronounced physiological action on the central nervous system.

Mycoatropine was first isolated by Schmeideberg in 1869, and the extraction technique was improved on by Kopp in 1899. Both workers also isolated muscarine, and at a later date at least two other alkaloids were identified, including choline which, in some subjects, produces gastrointestinal disturbance.

The individual actions of the various toxins synthesised by these fungi are still not wholly clear, but muscarine is no longer considered to be the principal hallucinogen present, as it occurs in measurably larger quantities in other fungi, where the physio-logical activity is markedly different.

Symptoms of mycoatropine poisoning appear any time from half an hour up to four hours after eating the fungus, causing nervous irritation and giddiness. The senses become heightened, and the subject may go into a trance–like state or become violently agitated. Death is uncommon; when it has occurred, the victim has been of particularly allergic nature, or already 'below par', in terms of general health.

4. *Muscarine poisoning.*

Although this alkaloid is synthesised by certain *Amanita* fungi, it is present in much greater concentrations in a number of other genera.

Many species of *Inocybe* synthesise muscarine, and it is found in the highest concentrations in three: *I. fastigiata, I. napipes,* and *I. patouillardii*. In other species like *I. maculata* the level is much lower.

Muscarine is also present in effective concentration in *Clitocybe dealbeata* (and *C. rivulosa,* if this turns out to be a distinct sub–species). In 1962, the journal *Science* reported the isolation of two drugs synthesised in the Mexican fungus, *Psilocybe mexicana,* which are thought to be closely related to muscarine; these two substances, psilocybin and psilocin, cause various mental aberrations and are used extensively by medicine men to induce trance–like states of awareness.

The lethal dose of muscarine, for an adult in the normal state of health, is between 0.3 and 0.5 gm. taken orally. A meal of less than 300 gm. fresh weight, even of the high concentration *Inocybe* species, would be unlikely to result in death.

Muscarine has a pronounced effect on the parasympathetic nervous system. Copious secretion is induced from tear and sweat glands, as well as from the mucous membranes of nose and throat, and from the pancreas. Sympathetic intestinal peristalsis is also strongly increased, and this is probably the cause of accompany-ing stomach cramps, vomiting and diarrhoea.

The nervous system is further affected, causing asthmatic breathing, double vision, narrowing of the pupils. The heart typically becomes slowed, with resulting loss of blood pressure and the sensation of cold in the hands and feet. In mild cases the symptoms subside quite quickly, but *in extremis* death can result from respiratory collapse, before which the victim usually becomes comatose.

Although many authorities have strongly opposed the practice, the cure for muscarine poisoning has been the administration of another naturally occurring alkaloid, atropine. Derived from deadly nightshade *(Atropa belladonna)*, this is given in 1–2 grain doses orally, in a tincture. Extreme cases have also been treated with atropine sulphate administered subcutaneously or intravenously.

5. *'Antabuse' intoxication.*

Several species of *Coprinus*, including *C. atramentarius* and *C. micaceus*, synthesise a substance described for convenience as 'antabuse'. This appears very similar to the man–made compound, tetraethylthiuramdisulphide, which has for some time been effectively employed in the treatment of chronic alcoholism.

These *Coprinus* species can be eaten with no ill effect, unless alcohol is taken with the meal or within several days following. When alcohol is consumed within these time limits, there is a very short incubation period of about twenty minutes followed by sudden flushing about the face. This rapidly extends to the neck and upper body, whilst the tip of the nose and the ear lobes remain characteristically pallid.

The pulse rate is dramatically increased, and the patient experiences great discomfort with the sensations of extreme heat in the affected parts. There is no stomach pain, vomiting, or diarrhoea, and the symptoms pass off rapidly, within an hour. There is no further effect, unless more alcohol is consumed, in which case the symptoms reappear, though with steadily decreasing intensity.

The mechanics behind the manifestation of symptoms when alcohol is taken are probably quite straightforward. The toxic principle is thought only to be readily soluble in alcohol, whilst being weakly soluble or even insoluble in aqueous media. The reappearance of symptoms with fresh intake of alcohol may well be attributable to the storage of the toxin in the liver, thence being released in part as the alcohol passes through the blood system.

Recent controlled experiments in the United States indicate that *C. atramentarius* may not be the culprit when the 'antabuse' syndrome appears. In a series of tests, an individual known for his ability to respond to the effects of alcohol was fed with various species, including the suspect *C. atramentarius*. These were eaten both in the raw state and cooked, in each case accompanied by alcohol.

The interesting result was that no outward effects of 'antabuse' poisoning were manifested. However, in a separate test, the individual was fed with a very small quantity of the fungus *Panaeolus*

campanulatus. In this instance, all the effects of 'antabuse' manifested themselves, even though no alcohol was consumed. The
genera favour similar habitats, and the suggestion was made that
they could be confused, thus giving *C. atramentarius* its bad name.

There seem to me to be a great many inconclusive loopholes
in this procedure, and the results were certainly far from con-
clusive. I fail to see how anyone with any knowledge of fungi
could seriously confuse *Coprinus atramentarius* or *C. micaceus* with
P. campanulatus. In any case, the essence of the 'antabuse' syndrome is that it only appears when the fungus is eaten in
conjunction with alcohol.

It seems far more likely that the researchers in this project
themselves fell foul of mistaken identity. This argument is sup-
ported by the prolific presence in the U.S.A. of a species *C. insignis,*
which possesses more or less identical gross morphological features.
It differs from *C. atramentarius* in producing spores that are verrucose, as opposed to smooth in the latter variety.

C. insignis is extremely rare in Europe, and to the best of my
knowledge it is not yet reported in the British Isles.

6. *The ergot toxins.*

The poisonous principles occurring in the fungus *Claviceps*
fall chiefly into the category of chemical compounds, known as
alkaloids. This term is applied to a number of substances found
in the plant kingdom, which are described as aromatic bases,
containing nitrogen. They are considered to be the end product
of nitrogen metabolism in certain plants and include a number of
drugs which have been extensively used in medicine, of which
cocaine, morphine, quinine and strychnine are perhaps the best
known.

Alkaloids are unknown in animal metabolism, and they all
have a pronounced physiological effect when taken into the body.
Whilst some, used in controlled amounts, can be beneficial, others
have purely adverse properties.

Six alkaloids have been isolated to date from *Claviceps,* which,
between them, affect normal body function in two ways:

(a) contractive stimulation of smooth muscle (eg. uterus,
blood vessels, stomach, and intestine).

(b) inhibitory action on the sympathetic function of the
nervous system.

The 'ergot' alkaloids are all derived from lysergic acid amide,
and the most important, physiologically, are ergotoxine, ergotine,
and ergotamine; of these, ergotamine has the ability to induce
contraction of the uterine muscle, even at very great dilution.

In addition to the alkaloids described above, *Claviceps* also
synthesises three physiologically active substances of a different
character. These are amines, ammonia derivatives in which one or
more of the hydrogen atoms become replaced by an alkyl radical.

Amine compounds isolated from the fungus include tyramine, which has a contractive (pressor) effect on smooth muscle; acetyl choline which has an inhibitive action on the heart; a histamine, which lowers blood pressure and also has a considerable stimulative effect on the uterus.

The effect of ingestion of these various principles over long periods is to produce a condition known as 'ergotism'.

In mild cases of ergotism, the subject experiences general tiredness and pains in the lower back or calves of the legs. There may be slight nausea and diarrhoea, but the appetite remains more or less normal. Some giddiness may also be experienced, but the symptoms generally disappear after two or three weeks.

However, in severe cases, brought about by prolonged intake of infected grain, two different forms of the disease are clearly distinguished.

(1) *Gangrenous ergotism.*

Initial symptoms as described above continue for two or three weeks, during the course of which one or more limbs become swollen and inflamed (legs seem more affected than arms).

The subject experiences symptoms in the affected part which alternate between icy cold and violent, burning heat. This condition is accompanied by great pain and may persist for some time or pass off quite rapidly. Gradually, however, the limb loses sensation, until it becomes quite numb.

At this point, the skin covering the affected area appears cyanosed, or bluish, and is cold to the touch. It may also erupt in reddish blisters, whilst over the rest of the body the skin takes on a yellow pallor, and the whites of the eyes also become yellowed.

Dry gangrene generally follows the numbing stage, and the affected part turns black, often with startling suddenness. Over a period of days, the gangrene slowly spreads inward along the limb, cutting off the blood supply as it advances.

If this stage of the disease is reached, surgery is necessary to amputate the limb. In instances where amputation has been delayed, there are records of the limb separating spontaneously at the joint.

Where a subject has lost a single limb (and provided ingestion of infected food is discontinued), recovery rate has been quite good, but the loss of two or more limbs has usually resulted in mortality within a few days. In extreme cases where all four limbs have been shed more or less simultaneously, the shock to the system has brought death very much more rapidly.

Some of the accounts on record are of a particularly gruesome nature. Barger described the supposedly factual account of a woman suffering from advanced gangrenous ergotism who was riding to hospital to have her leg amputated. The affected limb was accidentally caught against a bush beside the path and fell off at the knee. She continued to hospital, cradling the leg in her arms.

(2) *Convulsive ergotism.*

Initial symptoms are similar to those of gangrenous ergotism and can last for several weeks, though frequently accompanied by continuous sensations of 'pins and needles'. One authority quotes subjects as describing this 'like ants running about under the skin'. In typical cases, the feeling is limited to the fingers, but it can extend up the arms and even over the whole body, causing great distress when it attacks sensitive parts like lips, tongue, and genitalia.

If, after a few weeks, the symptoms are not alleviated, the disease generally enters a more acute phase. This commences with twitching of limbs, followed by convulsions and partial paralysis. If the subject is not confined to bed at this stage, he may exhibit a staggering walk, and the limbs become flexed to varying degrees. Indeed one of the most characteristic manifestations of the poisoning, often portrayed in old cartoons of affected persons, is the incurving of the hands and feet, giving them a claw–like appearance.

Curiously enough, the convulsions come on at fairly predict– able intervals; they may occur once or twice a week but are often at the same hour each day (generally during the morning), and they may even occur as close together as hourly. The attacks are accompanied by intense pain, and instances are on record where, during violent convulsions, the tongue has become badly lacerated or even completely bitten off.

Another symptom, of which there are some quite bizarre accounts, is that of ravenous hunger after the attacks. Barger cites a case where two patients ate a meal that apparently satisfied them momentarily, yet immediately afterwards each ate three pounds of bread in seven minutes. There are also reports of deranged victims eating clothing and, in extreme instances, scatophagy, or the consuming of faeces.

A further hazard was a form of catalepsy, in which patients would appear to be dead by all standards and only narrowly avoided being buried alive.

In fatal cases of convulsive ergotism, death usually occurs on the third or fourth day after the onset of severe symptoms; but in non–fatal cases, the convulsions, accompanied by delirium, may persist for a month or more. Even then, if the subject apparently returns to normal, minor convulsions and mental aberration may reoccur at intervals for many years after the initial attack. Children who fall victim may grow up seemingly fully recovered, only to become mad with the onset of puberty and finally die.

7. *The* Amanita *toxins.*

Taken as a whole, these chemicals represent some of the most dangerous compounds known to medical science, with regard to their pathological action on the human body.

Until very recently, when a remarkable breakthrough in the treatment of this type of poisoning was pioneered at King's College Hospital in London, chances of recovery after consuming *Amanita phalloides* were uncommon. When they did occur, it was more due to resistance of individuals than any clinical technique and depended largely on the amount of fungus consumed, amount of vomiting, and the general pre–poisoning health of the subject.

The toxins synthesised in the tissues of *A. phalloides* and its immediate relatives (or sub–species), *A. verna* and *A. virosa,* fall into two categories of organic compounds known as crystalline cyclo–peptides.

(a) Phallotoxins: these include the peptide phalloidin, first isolated from fresh fungal tissues in 1937, and several related compounds described as phalloin, phallicidin, phallisin, and phallin B. The compounds of this category are thermolabile, being destroyed by temperatures above 70°C., which means that their dangerous properties are lost with thorough cooking.

Phallotoxins are also rendered innocuous by weak acids and alkalis, including those found in the gut, secreted for the normal purposes of digestion.

Curiously, phalloidin, which occurs in the largest proportion of any toxin in the fungal tissue, is considered to be non–toxic in itself. Modern investigation has suggested that phalloidin is converted to a toxic compound by enzymes occurring in the liver, although the exact chemical make–up of this conversion com-pound is as yet unknown.

Phallin B has an intensely haemolytic effect on red blood cells, rapidly destroying them on contact. It is effective in extraordinarily minute quantities; for example, investigations indicate that the red cells of ox blood are haemolysed when phallin B is present in dilutions of one part in one hundred and twenty–five thousand (1:125,000).

Though the phallotoxins all act fairly rapidly on normal body physiology, they are considered not to be responsible for the extensive tissue destruction that characterises *A. phalloides* poisoning, and it is suggested that they are of account only when a small portion of the fungus is eaten raw, or in the event of it being included, uncooked, in a salad.

(b) Amanita toxins: the action of these compounds is far more severe than that of the previous group. However, they are much slower in action, and this almost certainly accounts for the twelve to fifteen hour delay normally encountered before any symptoms begin to manifest themselves.

The first pure compound of the type, amanitin, was isolated in 1941 and was subsequently resolved into a neutral α–amanitin, and an acidic β–amanitin. Since then at least four other related compounds have been isolated.

Unlike phallotoxins, which only attack blood, liver, kidney and heart cells, the amanita toxins destroy cells over the whole body. However, the site of their most intensive activity is the liver. They attack cell nuclei, and these begin to break up about fifteen hours after ingestion of the fungus, with the ensuing collapse of normal cell function and integrity. The time lapse is in itself one of the most dangerous factors of *A. phalloides* poisoning, because the poisons tend to be well dispersed through the body by the time any symptoms appear, and this renders first–aid treatment, such as stomach pumping, far less effective than it would be if the poisons were still confined to the gut.

Unlike the previous group of phallotoxins, the amanita toxins are thermostable and are not destroyed by normal cooking processes, nor are they affected by digestive juices.

Innumerable case histories show very similar patterns in the clinical progress of the poisoning, not just with regard to the symptoms manifested but to the time factor in each stage, which remains remarkably constant.

After the initial time lapse, the subject generally undergoes a period of intensive vomiting and diarrhoea but with no other outward indication of anything more amiss than a severe stomach upset. Towards the end of the first day, however, the skin of the subject may take on a grey or cyanosed pallor. Some cases are also noted in which the subject develops marked jaundice, and there are also instances where convulsions occur, indicating some damage to the central nervous system.

An unusual feature of the illness is that periods of remission frequently occur, during which the subject seems to be almost recovered. However, as a rule during the second day, peripheral circulatory failure becomes noticeable, and the pulse is greatly weakened, with almost total loss of recordable blood pressure.

At this juncture, chances of recovery are directly related to the amount of damage sustained by the liver cells. When the cell nuclei are destroyed, the integrity of the cell also breaks down and certain substances leak out through the cell membranes. Among these is the enzyme transaminase, and the extent of transaminase leakage can be measured. The normal transaminase, or S.G.O.T., leakage is up to 40 i.u. (international units) per litre. However, in liver malfunction this level can rise sharply. A French authority on fungal poisoning, Professor Benhamou, has indicated that if the S.G.O.T. is below 500 i.u./l., recovery is probable; 800–1000 i.u./l. possible; and over 1000 i.u./l. highly improbable. Total breakdown of all cell membranes in the liver will result in a leakage of some 8000 i.u./l.

Post–mortem studies on the victims of *A. phalloides* poisoning reveal certain specific areas of damage, dominated by massive deterioration of the liver and kidneys. These organs generally show considerable fatty degeneration, as also do the heart and diaphragm to a lesser degree. Abnormal amounts of fat may also be seen in pectoral, deltoid, and abdominal muscles, and in the tongue. A degree of haemorrhage may also be seen in the walls of the stomach and intestine, as well as the liver, kidneys and spleen.

Ford and Abel, during their researches into the pathology of *A. phalloides* poisoning, experimented freely by injecting the toxin into rabbits. By introducing the poison in this manner, all the characteristic features of fatty degeneration, tissue necrosis, haemorrhage etc, were induced in the expected manner. However, when Ford administered various extracts of the fungus by mouth, he was surprised to discover that the animals were wholly resistant to the action of the poisons. The exact mechanism by which the rabbit destroys amanita toxins in its gut is still unknown, but it would seem probable that its normal herbi–vorous habit helps to render it immune. Domestic carnivores, such as dogs and cats, are, by contrast, affected by the fungus in a similar manner to humans.

The immunity of the rabbit led to the bizarre, though widely adopted, treatment of feeding the poison victim with a mixture of three fresh stomachs and seven fresh brains of rabbit. This has all the ingredients of a witch doctor's ritual, but for many years great faith was attached to it by physicians in France, and it reportedly met with some degree of success.

Such then was the crude state of our knowledge and experi–ence of *A. phalloides* poisoning, and of effective therapy, until the autumn of 1973.

On the morning of October 14th 1973, Michael le Cocq and his wife Linda each ate five or six specimens of some fungi which they had collected the previous day from the lawn of an empty house on Guernsey.

Early the following morning, Dr C. J. Toynton of the Princess Elizabeth Hospital was called in to treat what he then thought to be a severe but otherwise typical attack of gastero–enteritis. The le Cocq's recounted eating the fungi, but left–over specimens revealed little by way of identification.

By October 16th both patients were extremely weak from the effect of repeated vomiting and diarrhoea, and obviously very ill. Michael le Cocq was, in fact, in a state of shock, with peripheral cyanosis, feeble pulse and low blood pressure. At this stage they were moved to hospital. At the same time, Dr Toynton was able to identify the fungi from a fresh crop which had appeared on the lawn as *Amanita phalloides*. His knowledge of mycology undoubtedly had an important bearing on the subsequent action which was taken, and assisted in saving the le Cocqs' lives.

Once hospitalised, both patients were administered massive volumes of sugar saline in an attempt to counter the severe dehydration of two days' vomiting and diarrhoea.

Hydrocortisone was also administered in high doses, to protect the liver from the expected necrosis.

In a routine procedure for the treatment of unusual poisons, the Poisons Centre at Guys Hospital, London, was contacted, and the Centre in turn alerted the Intensive Care Liver Unit at King's College Hospital, headed by Dr Roger Williams. The le Cocqs were flown to London on an emergency flight and transferred to the Unit, where tests showed that transaminase leakage was already in excess of 200 i.u./l. and was rising steadily.

Although he was much more collapsed at the gasteroenteritic stage of the poisoning than his wife, in the case of Michael le Cocq transaminase leakage only reached 800 i.u./l. (in itself a very dangerous level), and over the next few days, with sugar saline and hydrocortisone treatment, he began to recover, without going into hepatic coma. He was discharged eight days after eating the fungi, on October 25th.

His wife's condition became very critical, with severe liver damage and a recorded transaminase leakage of 2000 i.u./l., a figure at which death had hitherto been certain. She lapsed into a coma on October 19th. At that point, Dr Williams resorted to a hitherto almost untried technique, passing the patient's blood through a carbon column dialysis machine, recently pioneered at King's.

Linda le Cocq made medical history by regaining consciousness. Although she suffered extensive liver damage, modern therapeutic techniques enabled her to make a full recovery. She was discharged from the Intensive Care Unit on November 5th.

In May 1974, follow-up biopsies on the livers of both patients indicated that they had made full recovery and that the organs had regained normal morphology. There is now every chance that with artificial liver support systems like that pioneered at King's College Hospital with such dramatic effect, the incidence of mortality from accidentally eating this fungus may be greatly reduced. However, prompt diagnosis of *A. phalloides* poisoning will remain essential, to enable remedial treatment to be instigated before hepatic malfunction has continued too far.

*   *   *

In assessing the various types of fungal intoxication, it is possible to discern a number of common features attending the symptomatic course of poisoning.

A period of time, the incubation, always elapses between ingestion of the poisonous material and the manifestation of symptoms. Sensations of burning, or bitterness, or acridity may be experienced when an unwholesome fungus is eaten, and so give the first signs that something is amiss; but these are invariably short–lived, localised responses. The incubation period is not always of the same duration; symptoms may appear after as little as twenty minutes, or may, *in extremis,* be delayed for up to forty hours (Pilât).

Typically the first symptoms are vomiting and diarrhoea, with stomach pain; but if the toxins are not of a type affecting gastro–intestinal function, then these initial symptoms may take the form of nervous imbalance—for example, giddiness, increase in glandular secretion, heightened perception, general nervous distress, and so on.

A number of vital precautionary measures must be taken in a case of suspected fungus poisoning, but it is of paramount importance to get the victim under adequate medical supervision without delay.

The patient should be taken to hospital, rather than to a general practitioner, because the specific treatments needed in the case of severe fungal poisoning will necessitate specialised equip–ment and facilities, including blood transfusion, which will not be readily to hand in a doctor's surgery.

However, whilst on the way to hospital, or whilst awaiting an ambulance, the most essential first aid treatment is to try and prevent the toxins from spreading beyond the digestive tract into blood and other body tissues. The patient must be made to vomit even before seeing a doctor. There are two ways of achieving this, if a specific emetic is not to hand; the uvula at the back of the throat may be tickled with a finger or with some other convenient *soft* object, such as a feather; drinking large amounts of lukewarm, salty water may also produce the desired result, but not so quickly.

The patient may be in a state of nervous shock or excitement, if only at the thought of having consumed some poisonous matter, which in itself is not helpful as it can only cause increase in heart rate, so speeding up blood circulation and, with it, dispersal of any poison that has already entered the blood stream.

To counter this, the patient should be kept as still and as calm as possible. If the shock is severe, hot sweet tea is permissable; and if the heart becomes weak or fluttery, coffee may be admini–stered. Neither of these beverages will affect the rate of uptake of poison nor make it more difficult to remove. Alcohol, on the other hand, must *never* be administered in such cases, since it may have the effect of speeding up absorption of a toxin by increasing its solubility; this is manifestly the case with 'antabuse' poisoning.

Most of these points are really common sense, but there is one vital measure which may easily be overlooked in the confusion of the moment. The doctors endeavouring to treat the victim in hospital may have very little information to go on, with regard to specific therapeutic measures, unless the exact nature of the poisoning is known. To assist tracking down an unidentified source of poisoning, any stomach contents that the patient vomits must be retained for inspection, along with any uneaten part of

the meal (even if it must be dug out of the waste bin) and particu–
larly any uncooked specimens. If the patient is lucid enough to
describe where the specimens were found, or if this is already
known, then it may be very helpful to try and locate some fresh
specimens at the original site.

Above all, prompt and decisive action is essential. If someone
becomes at all unwell after eating fungi, do not hesitate to act at
once, because a life may depend on the promptness of others.

CHAPTER FIVE

The Poisonous Species

A great many instances of fungal poisoning can be put down to allergic reaction of the individual. Whereas one person can eat a particular specimen with immunity, another may experience indigestion or worse. I use the word 'poisonous' in its widest sense, and not necessarily in the dictionary sense of a substance which kills or injures when it enters the body. A more apt definition is 'departing from the normal state of health, when a small portion is consumed by a person susceptible to its effects'. After all, bear in mind, for reassurance if nothing else, that the number of *lethally* poisonous fungi, in the British Isles, can be counted on the fingers of one hand.

Apart from a personal factor in mushroom poisoning, the state of the specimen is always very important. As in many other forms of food, certain chemical changes occur with decomposition; poisonous substances, wholly absent in the young, fresh specimen, may appear with age, turning a good, harmless specimen into a dangerous one. J. Dearness states that the limit of edibility of a fungus is reached when worm tunnels can be detected with the naked eye, but I would prefer to avoid a specimen long before it reached that state.

CLAVICEPS PURPUREA (Fr.) Tulasne. Ergot of rye.

Habitat: the sclerotia appear during summer, in ears of infected rye grasses; they fall to the ground and germinate the following spring.

Dimensions: sclerotium 12–16 mm. long; up to 6 mm. thick.

Sclerotium: at first dull greyish, becoming purplish black when mature; fusiform and longitudinally furrowed. Flesh pallid, off–white, brittle in the dry state.

Stromata: arising from the sclerotium, microscopic, stalked with rounded capitula; at first yellow, becoming red, and finally purple; from ten to sixty appearing on each sclerotium. Spores purple, filiform, finally septate, 50 x 80 μ. long.

Odour: disagreeably of fish, in large concentrations of sclerotia.

Occurrence: common in some years on rye grasses, but also appearing on inflorescences of other Graminae. Host plant infected by ascospores well before the flowering period, and sclerotia mature shortly before harvesting time.

Ergot contains an alarming battery of substances, which have a pronounced physiological action on the human body. The chemistry and clinical action of these is detailed on pp. 168–171.

We are lucky that the advent of modern fungicides and careful screening of grain has almost eliminated the incidence of 'ergotism', though it still occurs in some far–flung districts of the USSR. However, it is a sobering thought that the ergot in the photograph was taken from a building site less than half a mile from my home in Sussex.

GYROMITRA ESCULENTA (Pers.) Fr.

Habitat: pine woods on sandy soils; solitary; on soil.

Dimensions: cap 2–7 cm. tall x 2–7 cm. dia.; stipe 3–7 cm. tall x 1.5–3.0 cm. dia.

Cap: at first chestnut brown, becoming darker, more date brown with age; rounded bulbous–inflated, partly connate with the stipe at the margin and partly remotely lobate, the whole plicate and cerebrally contorted. Flesh white, hollow.

Stipe: off–white, may be tinged yellowish or slightly aluta-ceous; plicate to scrobiculate in parts, glabrous. Flesh white, floccose, fragile. Spores hyaline, white in the mass, briefly ellip-soidal, smooth, 18–24 x 8–11 μ.

Odour: not distinctive.

Occurrence: very infrequent in the South, more common in the North. April–May.

Deaths have been constantly reported from eating this fungus, though precisely why remains a mystery.

It is true to say that both *Gyromitra* spp. and the related Helvellales synthesis helvellic acid, a dangerous haemolysing toxin which destroys red blood cells. However, it has been proven that under normal cooking processes this poison is rendered innocuous. Many people eat *Gyromitra esculenta* regularly with no unpleasant

179   *Claviceps purpurea*

effects, hence its specific name.

Nevertheless, the incidence of serious poisoning, and even death, is too high to include the fungus in the edible section, and it must be treated as strictly poisonous.

It cannot possibly be mistaken for any other species, and the incidence in the British Isles is too infrequent to warrant serious concern. It does not occur in the autumn months, being strictly vernal in appearance.

For further details of the action of the poison, see pp. 164–165.

HELVELLA ELASTICA Bull.

Habitat: mixed woods, favouring clay soils; singly, but often several closely scattered, on soil.

Dimensions: cap 1.5–3.0 cm. dia.; stipe 2–5 cm. tall x 4–6 mm. dia.

Cap: off–white, cream or very pale tan; saddle–shaped in two expanded lobes, deflected downwards, ·and lying freely adjacent to the stipe; flexuose, glabrous on lower (inner) surface; outer hymenial surface more greyish, and minutely pruinose. Flesh off–white, thin, elastic and brittle. Spores hyaline, white in the mass, briefly ellipsoid, smooth 18–20 x 10–12 μ.

Stipe: off–white above, more concolorous with cap at base and slightly pruinose, otherwise glabrous; cylindrical. Flesh off–white, elastic, brittle.

Odour: not distinctive.

Occurrence: occasional. June–October.

The Helvellas, like *Gyromitra,* synthesise the haemolytic toxin, helvellic acid. The percentage per dry weight in the tissues is probably a lot less, but in view of the dangers associated with eating *Gyromitra,* any members of the *Helvella* group should be left well alone, despite the fact that from time to time people will doubtless inform you that they are quite edible.

All species are instantly recognisable and can hardly be confused with any other fungal forms.

HELVELLA CRISPA (Scop.) Fr.

Habitat: frondose woods, favouring clay soils; singly but often several closely scattered; on soil.

Helvella elastica

Helvella c

Dimensions: cap 1.5–3.0 cm. dia.; stipe 2–5 cm. tall x 1–2 cm. dia.

Cap: pale greyish tan; saddle–shaped but irregularly folded and lobed, deflected more or less downwards and lying freely adjacent to stipe; glabrous on lower (inner) surface; outer hymenial surface minutely pruinose. Flesh off–white, thin, elastic and brittle. Spores hyaline, white in the mass, briefly ellipsoid, smooth 18–20 x 10–12 μ.

Stipe: off–white, extremely lacunose with raised branching and anastomosing ridges. Flesh off–white, hollow, brittle.

Odour: not distinctive.

Occurrence: locally common. August–October (may also appear in early spring).

HELVELLA LACUNOSA Afzel.

Habitat: mixed woods, favouring poor soils; singly but often closely scattered; on soil.

Dimensions: cap 2–4 cm. dia.; stipe 2–4 cm. tall x 1–2 cm. dia.

Cap: dark smokey grey, to blackish grey; basically bilobate but growing extremely irregular, may be upright or partly deflected back towards the stipe, lobate, folded; sterile (non–spore–bearing) surface glabrous, hymenial surface minutely pruinose. Flesh greyish, elastic, brittle, thin. Spores hyaline, white in the mass, briefly ellipsoid, smooth 15–16 x 10–12 μ.

Stipe: slightly paler than cap colour; extremely lacunose, with raised branching and anastomosing ridges; fleshy, hollow. Flesh greyish, elastic, brittle.

Odour: not distinctive.

Occurrence: fairly frequent. July–October.

RAMARIA FORMOSA (Fr.) Quél. Handsome clavaria.

Habitat: frondose woods; typically gregarious, on soil.

Dimensions: sporophore 10–20 cm. tall x 8–10 cm. dia.

Sporophore: at first pallid, becoming salmon pink or buff pink, and finally more or less ochraceous, except pedestal which remains pallid; tips of branches may be yellowish. Consisting of many branches arising from single, fleshy basal pedestal, the terminal branchlets extremely numerous and dentate or bifurcate. Flesh fragile, at first pallid, becoming tinged pink and finally more or less ochraceous. Hymenium spread over branches; spores

Helvella lacu

yellowish, ellipsoidal, slightly rugose, 9–12 x 4–5 μ.
Odour: not distinctive. **Taste:** somewhat bitter.
Occurrence: infrequent. August–October.

Although a number of the *Ramaria* and *Clavaria* species are generally considered to be suspect, this is the only one which is positively so labelled, on account of its extremely acrid taste. It is unfortunately very similar in appearance to *R. botrytis,* which is edible, so it is necessary to taste a small quantity in order to ascertain which is which!

AGARICUS XANTHODERMUS Genevier. Yellow staining mushroom.

Habitat: woods generally; solitary; on soil.
Dimensions: cap 5–10 cm. dia.; stipe 6–10 cm. tall x 1–2 cm. dia.
Cap: white at first, becoming alutaceous and greyish with age, darker towards disc; at first campanulate, becoming plane or slightly depressed; cuticle smooth, glabrous, silky shining in dry weather, frequently with remnants of veil adhering to margin. Flesh white, turning chrome yellow where cut; firm and moderately thick.
Gills: at first pallid, finally chocolate brown with purple tinge, never pink. Spores chocolate brown with purple tinge, ovate, smooth 5–6 x 3–4 μ.
Stipe: white at first, yellowing in older specimens, smooth, silky, relatively slender, bulbous at base. Note: this species and a related poisonous species, *A. placomyces,* are the only two members of the family where the flesh at the base of the stipe is chrome yellow *immediately* on cutting. Flesh white at first, becoming generally yellow in older specimens, soft, rapidly becoming cavernose.
Odour: of ink or phenol, becming very acrid on cooking.
Occurrence: fairly frequent. August–October.

It is unfortunate that two members of the *Agaricus* family possess toxic principles which, whilst not deadly, can induce a nasty stomach upset.
Do not be misled into believing that *Agaricus* spp. that bruise yellow are all poisonous, as many of the edible ones share this distinction. The main criterion is that only *A. xanthoderma* and *A. placomyces* appear *immediately* discoloured yellow when the *extreme base* of the stipe is cut.

185

Agaricus xanthoder

They also share an unpleasant smell said to be reminiscent of writing ink, or phenol, unlike most of the more palatable varieties which smell of aniseed.

The poisons involved do not disappear on cooking, but they are not considered to be in the dangerously poisonous category. At most the victim will probably suffer an acute bout of gastro-enteritis.

A particularly useful chemical test which positively isolates *A. xanthoderma* from the edible members is as follows:

Thallium oxide 2.0 gm.	sodium bicarbonate 1 gm.
conc. hydrochloric acid 4.0 ml.	distilled water 10 ml.
conc. nitric acid 1.0 ml.	

The cap cuticle of *A. arvensis* and *A. silvicola* turns red, whilst that of *A. xanthoderma* does not react.

AMANITA MUSCARIA (L. ex Fr.) Hooker. Fly agaric; Muscarine agaric.

Habitat: found generally in both frondose and coniferous woods, but more typical under birch; shows preference for poor, sandy soils.

Dimensions: cap 8–18 cm. dia.; stipe 12–20 cm. tall x 1.5–2.5 cm. dia.

Cap: at first deep scarlet, shining; may remain this colour or fade; covered with irregular, white, warty fugacious patches, easily washed off. Older specimens typically orange and patches may be absent. Sub-spherical at first, becoming convex and finally plano–expanded, to slightly depressed. Margin slightly sulcate when mature. Pigment under cap cuticle golden yellow, flesh otherwise white.

Gills: white, free, broad, and crowded. Spores white, hyaline, ellipsoidal, smooth 10–12×6–$7\,\mu$.

Stipe: white to pale cream with surface sculpturing; at first solid, then hollow. Annulus high on the stem, having distinct double margin with ragged edge to inner layer; closely pendant. Base moderately bulbous with two or three rings of warty volval remains immediately above.

Odour: not distinctive.

Occurrence: common and in some years prolific. August–November.

Of all our native fungi, this must surely be the most familiar, its pretty appearance making it a favourite subject for children's stories. Yet the prettiness is a cover, and the fungus has more

188   *Amanita muscaria* (mature sporoph

Amanita muscaria (old sporophore)

sinister connotations as the vehicle for a complex of dangerous, sometimes fatal, mind drugs.

So complicated are the toxins synthesised that neither their action nor their extent are as yet fully understood. At one time the fungus was considered to contain a single hallucinogenic poison, muscarine, responsible not only for inducing a trance—like state but also sweat, tears, palpitations. It also kills flies, hence 'fly agaric'.

However, it is known today that at least four toxic principles are active in the tissues of fresh specimens, all of which produce markedly different physiological effects.

Although, as far as I can establish, the practice of eating fly agaric has never been recorded in the British Isles, something of a cult has grown up around it in parts of Siberia, where it is valued by the Koryaks of Kamchatka as an hallucinogen and is used by the Kanchdal as the basis for a fermented beverage.

AMANITA PANTHERINA (DC ex Fr.) Secr. Panther cap.

Habitat: typically occurring at edges of frondose woods, favours beech.

Dimensions: cap 6–10 cm. dia.; stipe 6–12 cm. tall x 1.5–2.5 cm. dia.

Cap: dull brown, varying through yellowish, olive, or grey brown, typically darker at the centre; silky with faint radiating fibrils when dry, slightly viscid when moist; covered at first with white, irregular velar patches, easily fugacious. At first sub–spherical, then convex, and finally plano–expanded. Margin sulcate, thin. Flesh white.

Gills: white, free, crowded, unequally broad, and ventricose. Spores white, hyaline, ellipsoidal, smooth 10–12 x 6–7 μ.

Stipe: white, smooth and silky, fibrillose, at first solid, then hollow. Annulus white, about mid–way on stem, narrow with double margin, often fugacious. Base only slightly bulbous with two or three circles of squamular volval remnants between it and the annulus.

Odour: not distinctive.

Occurrence: very infrequent. August–October.

The fungus is extremely poisonous and contains toxins similar to those found in *Amanita muscaria*. However, muscarine is present in much higher concentrations, and it now appears that this is the lethal alkaloid, whilst mycoatropine induces hallucina–tion and its attendant symptoms.

According to Smith (1949) *Amanita pantherina* has been

190

responsible for many more deaths in Europe than *A. muscaria* when it may well have been eaten in mistake for *A. rubescens,* the edible blusher!

The fungus does not, however, contain any of the slow—acting cyclo—peptide toxins found in *A. phalloides* and *A. virosa,* and symptoms manifest themselves very quickly. Violent stomach pains are followed by vomiting and diarrhoea. The patient feels very dizzy and disorientated. In fatal cases, death is usually pre—ceeded by convulsions and coma.

AMANITA PHALLOIDES (Vaill. ex Fr.) Secr. Death cap.

Habitat: light frondose and coniferous woods, fringes of woods, copses etc; particularly favouring oak, often in bracken; solitary or scattered; on soil.

Dimensions: cap 7–15 cm dia.; stipe 5–10 cm. tall x 0.8–2.0 cm. dia.

Cap: very variable in colour, basically greenish tan, but can be olive or greenish yellow; at first campanuliform, becoming expanded-convex; cuticle always characteristically streaked with slightly darker radiating fibrils, slightly viscid when wet, silky striate when dry, often with whitish 'bloom', mature cap typically lacking velar remains. Flesh slightly tinged cap colour beneath cuticle, otherwise white, medium.

Gills: white, free, ventricose, slightly rounded proximally, crowded. Spores hyaline, white in the mass, sub–spherical, smooth, 8–10 μ.

Stipe: faintly tan with surface sculpturing; annulus high on the stem, irregularly torn, upper surface at first sulcate; base very bulbous with lobate volva extending upwards, often as far as the annulus, in a loose, uneven sheath. Flesh white, at first full, becoming floccose or hollow. Note: it is of considerable import—ance to appreciate that the lower 'ring' or base of volval sheath may actually be subterranean in many specimens. It is necessary, therefore, to dig up the whole specimen, including the basal bulb to be sure of this crucial identification feature.

Odour: not distinctive.

Chemical tests: conc. sulphuric acid on gills turns pale lilac at once (this test is supposed to be specific for *A. phalloides,* but the non—function in other species is not yet confirmed).

Occurrence: not common in the British Isles, though more prolific in certain years. August–November.

Although the incidence of *A. phalloides* is limited in Britain, it is far more prolific in the Channel Islands and France, where

Amanita phalloides (young sporoph

193   *Amanita phalloides* (mature sporophore)

many cases of poisoning occur each year.

As its name implies, the 'death cap' is intensely poisonous, and up until very recently there has been little chance of recovery once its toxic principles are absorbed into the blood above a certain level.

Within the last few years, there has been a remarkable breakthrough in the successful treatment of *A. phalloides* poisoning, with the case of Linda and Michael le Cocq. This is referred to in detail on pp. 173–174 in the chapter dealing with fungal chemistry.

AMANITA CITRINA [Schaeff.] Gray. False death cap.

Habitat: woods generally; scattered solitary; on soil.
Dimensions: cap 4–10 cm. dia.; stipe 5–10 cm. tall x 1.0–2.0 cm. dia.
Cap: variable from lemon yellow to wholly white; at first hemispherical becoming expanded–convex; cuticle bears patches of velar remains, otherwise glabrous; not striate or fibrillose. Flesh white medium.
Gills: white, free, crowded. Spores hyaline, white in the mass, sub–globose, smooth, 8–10 x 7–8 μ.
Stipe: white, smooth, glabrous; annulus firm, high on the stem; base bulbous, but volval rim very reduced, forming a ridge only, and not a volval sheath. Flesh white, at first full becoming stuffed or hollow.
Odour: distinctly of raw potato, when flesh is broken.
Occurrence: common and widespread. August–November.

Frequently confused with the true death cap, *A. phalloides*, this fungus is unpleasant to eat but non–poisonous. It is included here because of the frequent confusion between the two species.

CLITOCYBE DEALBEATA (Sow. ex Fr.) Kümmer.

Habitat: lawns, parks, pastures with short grass, favouring rich soils; gregarious, frequently in rings, on soil.
Dimensions: cap 2–5 cm. dia.; stipe 2–4 cm. tall x 4–8 mm. dia.
Cap: off–white to cream or pale tan, sometimes with faint pinkish or lilac tones; at first convex becoming flattened to slightly

Amanita citrina

depressed at disc, with margin involute in all but old specimens, which are wholly plane or irregular; cap cuticle dry, smooth, glabrous, but pruinose at the margin when young, may be faintly zoned concentrically. Flesh white, firm.

Gills: pallid at first, becoming pale pinkish buff, slightly decurrent, crowded. Spores hyaline, white in the mass, ovate or ellipsoidal, smooth, 4–6 x 2.5–3.5 μ.

Stipe: concolorous with cap, shorter than cap diameter, slightly tomentose above. Flesh white, firm, full.

Odour: not distinctive.

Occurrence: common. August–November.

C. *dealbeata* is the only British species of the genus known to be poisonous. There is some confusion as to whether a separate specie, C. *rivulosa,* exists; if it does, then it also shares dangerous properties, but the majority of authorities reject its occurrence — the two are, by any account, so alike as to be more or less indistinguishable.

C. *dealbeata* synthesises muscarine, in common with most of the *Inocybe* species and some *Amanita* species. The effects of poisoning are serious and, if enough of the fungus is ingested, can be fatal.

Details of the effects are given on pp. 166–167.

It is best to steer well clear of any small, whitish species of *Clitocybe,* because a number of other types with these characteristics are thought to be dangerous.

COPRINUS ATRAMENTARIUS Bull. ex Fr. 'Antabuse' agaric; Common ink cap.

Habitat: fields and gardens, also waste patches, often pushing up through gravel and tarmac; typically in dense caespitose clumps round or on bases of frondose stumps, or on submerged wood; less frequently near living trees.

Dimensions: cap 3–7 cm. dia.; stipe 5–11 cm. tall x 1.0–2.0 cm. dia.

Cap: dirty greyish brown to brown; at first ovate with margin adpressed to stipe, becoming campanulate; cuticle rusty squamulose at disc, otherwise more or less glabrous, sulcate or radically wrinkled. Cap autodigests from margin, becoming deliquescent, leaving small, plano–expanded vestige at disc, often with revolute margin. Flesh white.

Gills: at first off–white, rapidly becoming dirty brown, and finally black. Spores brown, black in the mass, ovate, smooth, 7–11 x 5–7 μ.

Coprinus atramentarius

Stipe: off–white, smooth, slender and attenuated upwards, rapidly elongating; no annulus; slightly swollen base terminates at distinct line. Flesh white, hollow.

Odour: not distinctive.

Occurrence: common. June–November.

Both this fungus and the related specie *C. micaceus* described overleaf pose something of a dilemma with regard to their edibility. However, I have decided to play safe and to include them both in the poisonous category.

In fact, *C. atramentarius* is edible and many people do collect it for the table. It unfortunately seems to produce peculiar and unpleasant symptoms if consumed with alcohol, or if alcohol is subsequently taken for several days after eating. There is some dispute as to whether the specie is wrongly maligned and obtains its bad name from cases of mistaken identity, but fuller discussion is given to both effects and possible causes on pp. 167–168.

I think the matter is sufficiently in doubt and that it should be left well alone, particularly if you are partial to an occasional drink!

COPRINUS MICACEUS Fr.

Habitat: on or around stumps of frondose trees, in very varied situations, frequently pushes up through soft asphalt of pave–ments and drives; densely caespitose; on wood which may be subterranean.

Dimensions: cap 1–4 cm. dia.; stipe 3–5 cm. tall x 0.5–0.75 cm. dia.

Cap: typically date brown, may be more tawny or ochre brown; at first ovate, with margin adpressed to stipe, becoming more broadly conical, finally obtusely conical to expanded with somewhat revolute margin; cuticle moist, deeply sulcate, covered with fugaceous mica–like particles. Flesh pale buff, fragile, thin.

Gills: at first white, soon tinged vinaceous grey, and finally purplish black, adnate, crowded, fairly broad. Spores dark purp–lish brown, black in the mass, sub–ovate, smooth, 7–9 x 4–5 μ.

Stipe: pallid, at first covered with dense, very short hairs, then more or less glabrous. Flesh pallid, medium. No annulus.

The fungus undergoes limited autodigestion.

Odour: not distinctive.

Occurrence: common. June–November.

Coprinus micaceus

ENTOLOMA SINUATUM (RHODOPHYLLUS) *(Bull. ex Fr.) Kümmer.
*Singer.

Habitat: light, open frondose woods, edges of woods, favour–
ing oak and beech; gregarious or scattered; on soil.
Dimensions: 5–15 cm. dia.; stipe 4–12 cm. tall x 0.5–3.0 cm.
dia.
Cap: pale greyish cream; at first campanulate–convex,
becoming irregular expanded with broad umbo; cuticle glabrous,
shining, may be slightly viscid in damp weather, cracking radially
at the margin in older specimens. Flesh white, medium, firm.
Gills: at first cream colour, becoming salmon pink, adnate
becoming more or less free with maturity, broad, distant. Spores
sub–spherical, regularly hexagonal in cross section, salmon pink,
9–11 x 9 μ.
Stipe: white, silky fibrillose, pruinose under the cap, attenu–
ated upwards, generally shorter than cap diameter and typically
flexuose. Flesh white, full, thick.
Odour: mildly farinose.
Occurrence: infrequent. September–November.

Little is known at present about the poisonous principles of
this fungus, but it owes its notoriety largely to a resemblance, in
some stages of development, to the edible field mushroom.
Entoloma sinuatum grows prolifically in the south of France, and
in some regions it is given the inspiring title of 'le grand empoison–
neur de la Côte d'Or'.
Effects of poisoning are rarely fatal, but the symptoms can
persist for a long time making the patient extremely weak, and
death, when it does occur, probably results from general ex–
haustion and shock. Symptoms usually start between one and
two hours after eating and involve intense gastro–intestinal
disturbance with prolonged vomiting and diarrhoea. There is
typically acute abdominal pain and excessive sweating.
Although poisoning is hardly a subject for levity, I have
come across one gem of Victorian rhetoric in connection with
this fungus. It is a first hand account of poisoning by the redoubt–
able toadstool epicure, Worthington Smith, extracted from his
book *Mushrooms and Toadstools* (Hardwicke 1867). He refers to
'Entoloma fertilis' in the text, but having studied the water–colour
drawing attached, I am left in little doubt that the fungus he
described is *E. sinuatum*:
'Without doubt a furiously poisonous plant, for I once cooked
a very small piece for luncheon, and was very nearly poisoned to
death thereby. Taste by no means disagreeable, but mark the
result.
'About a quarter of an hour after luncheon, I left home and

was immediately overcome by a strange nervous, gloomy, low—spirited feeling, quite new to me. Soon a severe headache added its charms to my feelings, and then swimming of the brain commenced, with violent pains in the stomach.

'I now had great difficulty to keep upon my legs at all; my senses all appeared leaving me, and every object appeared to be moving with death—like stillness from side to side, up and down, or round and round.

'More dead than alive, I soon returned home, and was horrified to find two others (whom I had invited to partake of my repast) in exactly the same condition as myself. At this moment and not before, I thought of Entoloma fertilis. These two others had suffered precisely as I had done, and we all three were apparently dying fast. They, however, were attacked by fearful vomiting, which I imagine helped hasten their recovery, for after a few days of sickness and nausea (with medical assistance) they got well; but it was not so with me, for although I had at first the inclination, I had not the strength left to vomit.

'During the latter part of the first day, I was however so continually and fearfully purged, and suffered so much from headache and swimming of the brain, that I really thought every moment would be my last. I was very ill for the next four to five days; suffered from loathing and lassitude; fell into deep sleep, long and troubled; at times found all my joints quite stiff; at others everything would be swimming before me; and it was not until a fortnight had elapsed that every bodily derangement had left me.'

If one puts aside the magnificent drama of this account, it provides a rather chilling example of why it is necessary to distinguish between this fungus and the edible mushroom.

What are the important differences? Most important, the *Agaricus* group are distinguished by possession of an annulus on the stem. However, this can easily have fallen off in older specimens. *Agaricus* gills are mostly pink from the outset, finally becoming chocolate brown, whereas those of *Entoloma* start life a yellowish cream colour, and then turn salmon pink in the mature cap. Generally speaking though, the mushroom types with which it can be confused grow well away from trees, in open fields and roadsides, and the only similar—looking species to be found under trees, *Agaricus silvicola*, smells distinctly of aniseed.

HEBELOMA CRUSTULINIFORME (Bull. ex St. Amans) Quél.

Habitat: mixed woods, also appearing in gardens; scattered or one or two caespitose; on soil.
Dimensions: cap 3–7 cm. dia.; stipe 3–7 cm. tall x 1.0–1.5 cm. dia.

Cap: pale whitish tan, typically darker at the disc; at first convex–campanulate with involute margin, becoming expanded–convex sometimes with obtuse umbo; cuticle at first slightly viscid with finely velvety margin, becoming more dull, smooth, glabrous. Flesh off–white, firm, thick.

Gills: at first off–white, becoming pale alutaceous, and finally dull date brown; adnexed, narrow, crowded, thin, generating watery drops in wet weather, leaving brown spots when dry. Spores dull date brown, ovate, smooth to minutely pruinose, $10–12 \times 5–8\,\mu$.

Stipe: off–white, stout, at times somewhat bulbous, squamulose at the apex, otherwise smooth, glabrous. Flesh concolorous, stuffed, becoming hollow, fairly firm.

Odour: strongly of radish.

Occurrence: common. August–November.

H. crustuliniforme and the following species *H. sinuosum* are both members of a family which is to be considered suspect, though they are the only two species large enough to warrant inclusion.

Both are extremely indigestible, causing stomach cramps and sickness, and in the case of *H. crustuliniforme* the strong, characteristic smell of radish is retained on cooking, making the fungus unpalatable.

The family are all characterised by tan, or pallid, rather viscid caps and dull brown gills at maturity.

HEBELOMA SINUOSUM (Fr.) Quél.

Habitat: mixed woods, favouring damp locations; typically solitary; on soil.

Dimensions: cap 5–12 cm. dia.; stipe 5–12 cm. tall x 1.0–2.0 cm. dia.

Cap: pale tan or whitish flesh colour; at first convex becoming expanded; cuticle typically viscid, smooth, glabrous. Flesh off–white, firm, thick.

Gills: at first off–white, becoming pale alutaceous, and finally dull date brown; adnexed, narrow, crowded, without velar remains. Spores dull date brown, ovate, smooth, $10–12 \times 5–6\,\mu$.

Stipe: pallid with characteristic closely adpressed scaly zones; base somewhat bulbous, rooting. Flesh concolorous, stuffed, becoming hollow, fairly firm.

Odour: not distinctive.

Occurrence: infrequent. September–October.

203

Hebeloma sinuosum

INOCYBE ASTEROSPORA Quél.

Habitat: very variable in frondose woods, parks, verges of woodland paths, etc; solitary or scattered; on soil.
Dimensions: cap 2–5 cm. dia.; stipe 5–8 cm. tall x 0.5–1.0 cm. dia.
Cap: bay brown, or dirty cinnamon brown; at first campanulate, becoming expanded–umbonate; cuticle rimose, fibrillose with darker brown fibrils. Flesh pallid, thin.
Gills: at first pallid, becoming cinnamon brown, free, more or less ventricose. Spores dull brown, sub–spherical, bluntly echinate, $10-13\,\mu$.
Stipe: brown fibrillose–striate on pallid background, slender, but base somewhat bulbous, terminating in distinct margin. Flesh pallid.
Odour: not distinctive, or faintly farinose.
Occurrence: occasional. September–October.

It is quite probable that practically all species of *Inocybe* synthesise the alkaloid muscarine and hence, as a group, must be avoided. The percentage of muscarine in the tissues determines whether a particular specie is dangerous or even deadly. An adult in good health needs to consume about half a gram of muscarine before death is probable, and three species would meet this requirement if a typical meal of the fungi were consumed. These are *I. fastigiata, I. napipes,* and *I. patouillardii.*

Inocybes are not particularly conspicuous fungi, mostly being on the small size and typically of a rather uninteresting brownish colour; the caps are typically campanulate or umbonate and almost invariably are distinctly radially fibrillose. The young caps display a cobwebby cortina covering the gills, and the fungi usually smell earthy or less frequently fruity. Spores are dull date brown and give a distinctive colouring to the mature gills.

INOCYBE FASTIGIATA (Schaeff. ex Fr.) Quél.

Habitat: frondose woods and copses; solitary or scattered; on soil.
Dimensions: cap 3–6 cm. dia.; stipe 4–9 cm. tall x 1.0–1.5 cm. dia.
Cap: yellowish brown to yellowish ochre, pale; at first conical–campanulate, becoming conical to conical–expanded with acute umbo; cuticle rimose, fibrillose, very often radially

cracked at the margin. Flesh pallid, thin.

Gills: at first yellow becoming brownish olive, free, crowded. Spores dull brown, ovate, smooth, 9–10 x 5.5–7.5 μ.

Stipe: pallid yellow or off–white, stoutish, often a little flexuose, longer than cap diameter, at first finely villose or tomen–tose, becoming wholly minutely fibrillose. Flesh off–white, full.

Odour: earthy farinose.

Occurrence: fairly common. July–October.

INOCYBE GEOPHYLLA (Sow. ex Fr.) Kümmer.

Habitat: mixed woods, favouring damp soils; scattered or in small groups; on soil.

Dimensions: cap 1.5–3.0 cm. dia.; stipe 4–7 cm. tall x 0.5–0.75 cm. dia.

Cap: wholly white, may be tinged yellowish when old; at first conical, becoming expanded and sharply umbonate; cuticle minutely fibrillose silky, often cracking radially, may bear remnants of cortina at margin. Flesh white, thin.

Gills: pallid, becoming dingy clay colour, adnexed or more or less free, broad, crowded, ventricose, covered at first with cortina. Spores dull brown, ellipsoidal, smooth, 7–9 x 4–5 μ.

Stipe: white, typically somewhat flexuose, slightly thickened at base, minutely floccose at the apex, otherwise satiny smooth. Flesh white, stuffed, thin.

Odour: earthy or slightly farinose.

Occurrence: common. July–October.

INOCYBE GRISEOLILACINA Lange.

Habitat: frondose woods, parks, etc; solitary or scattered; on soil.

Dimensions: cap 1–3 cm. dia.; stipe 4–7 cm. tall x 0.3–0.5 cm. dia.

Cap: pale greyish brown, somewhat darker at disc; conical-convex, not obviously umbonate; cuticle sub–squamulose, or shaggy–fibrillose. Flesh pallid with lilac tinge, thin, delicate.

Gills: pale lilac, becoming dull brown, free, crowded. Spores dull brown, ovate–ellipsoidal, smooth, 9–10 x 4–5 μ.

Stipe: pale lilac covered with whitish flocci and fibrils, without basal bulb. Flesh pallid with lilac tinge, delicate.

Odour: faintly earthy–farinose.

Occurrence: occasional. September–October.

INOCYBE JURANA Pat.

Habitat: frondose woods; loosely gregarious; on soil.
Dimensions: cap 4–8 cm. dia.; stipe 5–8 cm. tall x 1.0–1.5 cm. dia.
Cap: rufous, tinged fuscous or vinaceous; at first conical-campanulate, becoming expanded umbonate; cuticle markedly fibrillose except at disc which is typically smooth or squamulose, margin may be cracked radially. Flesh off–white, tinged fuscous under cuticle.
Gills: at first off–white, becoming yellowish or greyish umber; often spotted; sinuate, almost free, crowded, covered at first with cortina. Spores dull brown, sub–reniform, smooth, 10–12 x 6–8 μ.
Stipe: off–white at the apex, otherwise tinged fuscous, or vinaceous, sub–floccose at the apex, otherwise fibrillose. Flesh pallid but tinged as cap flesh, at apex and in base, stuffed.
Odour: earthy farinose.
Occurrence: uncommon. August–November.

INOCYBE LACERA (Fr.) Kümmer.

Habitat: mixed woods and heaths, favouring pine; loosely gegarious; on soil.
Dimensions: cap 2–3 cm. dia.; stipe 3–5 cm. tall x 0.5–0.75 cm. dia.
Cap: dull date brown, or mousey, occasionally tinged olivaceous at the margin; at first convex with central papilla, becoming expanded and obtusely umbonate; cuticle at first fibrillose, becoming squamulose to squarrose. Flesh pallid, dull brown, thin.
Gills: at first pinkish olive grey, becoming more mousey, and finally olive brown; sinuate–adnexed, not crowded, broad, covered at first with cortina. Spores dull brown, fusiform, smooth, 9–11 x 5.0–5.5 μ.
Stipe: concolorous with cap cuticle, but paler, covered with darker brownish fibrillose flecks; slender, attenuated downwards. Flesh rust brown, thin.
Odour: not distinctive.
Occurrence: fairly frequent. July–September.

INOCYBE MACULATA Boud.

Habitat: frondose woods; loosely gregarious; on soil.
Dimensions: cap 3–5 cm. dia.; stipe 3–8 cm. tall x 1.0–1.5 cm. dia.
Cap: dark brown rimose fibrils on whitish background, with pallid adpressed squamules, more or less concentrically arranged at disc; at first campanulate, becoming expanded umbonate. Flesh off–white, thin.
Gills: at first fawn, tinged olive, finally dull date brown; more or less free, broad. Spores dull brown, oblong–ellipsoidal, smooth, 10–13 x 5–6 μ.
Stipe: concolorous with pileus, but paler at apex, striate–fibrillose, scurfy at apex, slightly thickened at the base. Flesh off–white, full.
Odour: slightly fruity.
Occurrence: common. September–November.

INOCYBE NAPIPES Lange.

Habitat: damp ground, favouring birch bogs; solitary or scattered; on soil.
Dimensions: cap 3–5 cm. dia.; stipe 5–6 cm. tall x 0.5–0.75 cm. dia.
Cap: brownish umber, or chestnut; at first conical-campanulate, becoming expanded and acutely umbonate; cuticle minutely rimose–fibrillose with dark brown fibrils. Flesh pallid, thin.
Gills: at first pallid, becoming yellowish brown, free, crowded. Spores dull brown, ovate, nodulose, 9–10 x 5–6 μ.
Stipe: concolorous with cap cuticle, paler under cap, minutely fibrillose; slender with basal bulb not terminating in margin. Flesh pallid.
Odour: faintly farinose.
Occurrence: occasional and very localised. September–October.

INOCYBE PATOUILLARDII (Bres.) Red staining inocybe.

Habitat: light frondose woods, favouring beech and lime; singly, or in small groups, occasionally one or two caespitose, on soil.

Inocybe mac.

Inocybe patouillardii

Dimensions: cap 3–8 cm. dia.; stipe 3–8 cm. tall x 1–2 cm. dia.

Cap: at first off–white, soon dirty whitish grey, becoming yellowish brown, turning pinkish red where bruised, old specimens may be stained reddish more generally; at first conical–campanulate, becoming expanded and moderately umbonate, margin at first involute, becoming cracked radially as cap expands; cuticle silky fibrillose, dry. Flesh at first more or less white, becoming yellowish and finally yellowish brown, turning pinkish red where cut, firm.

Gills: at first off–white, becoming olive yellow, and finally olive brown to cinnabar, may be spotted reddish; edge of gill at first white floccose, from fugacious white coriacious veil; adnate to sinuate, crowded, fairly narrow. Spores pale brown, darker clay brown in the mass, ovate, smooth 9–14 x 5–8 μ.

Stipe: concolorous with cap, but paler in mature specimens, also bruising pinkish red; cylindrical to slightly attenuated above; at first pruinose above otherwise smooth and glabrous. Flesh concolorous with that of cap, moderately thick, full, fibrillar.

Odour: unpleasant.

Occurrence: occasional. May–September.

One of the most dangerous of the *Inocybe* family, an important clue when trying to identify *I. patouillardii* is the characteristic reddening of the flesh where it is cut or damaged.

In spite of the fact that most Inocybes do not look even remotely appetising, a death was recorded in Surrey in 1937 from eating this fungus, and on a previous instance some soldiers who ate smaller quantities experienced symptoms of dizziness, vomiting and profuse sweating.

INOCYBE PRAETERVISA Quél.

Habitat: very variable in frondose woods, parks, verges of woodland paths etc; solitary or scattered; on soil.

Dimensions: cap 3–6 cm. dia.; stipe 4–7 cm. tall x 0.5–0.75 cm. dia.

Cap: ochraceous tan, darkening towards disc; at first conical–campanulate, becoming expanded and broadly umbonate, with flexuose margin typically at maturity; cuticle rimose, fibrillose, may be cracked radially at the margin. Flesh pallid thin.

Gills: pallid, becoming pale cinnamon, almost free, crowded. Spores dull brown, ovate, nodulose, 10–11 x 5–6 μ.

Stipe: pale yellowish straw colour, sub–fibrillose and slightly pruinose at the apex, base minutely bulbous, terminating in

Inocybe praetervisa

distinct margin. Flesh pallid, full.

Odour: farinose.

Occurrence: occasional. September–October.

INOCYBE SQUAMATA Lange.

Habitat: favouring poplars on rich clay soils, generally by edges of woods and copses, underneath hedges etc; solitary or in small groups; on soil.

Dimensions: cap 3–7 cm. dia.; stipe 3–5 cm. tall x 0.5–1.0 cm. dia.

Cap: tawny ochre, usually darker at disc; at first concial-convex, becoming conical–expanded, sometimes but not always with umbo; fibrillose, at disc more squamulose, areolate, or smooth. Flesh pallid.

Gills: pale tawny with olivaceous tinge; sinuate, broad, distant. Spores dull brown, ovate, smooth, 9.5–12.0 x 5.5–6.5 μ.

Stipe: more or less concolorous with cap cuticle, fibrillose. Flesh yellowish pallid, stuffed then partly hollow.

Odour: not distinctive.

Occurrence: strictly localised and therefore rare. September–October.

LACTARIUS BLENNIUS (Fr. & Fr.) Fr.

Habitat: frondose woods; solitary, or loosely scattered; on soil.

Dimensions: cap 4–10 cm. dia.; stipe 4–5 cm. tall x 1.0–2.0 cm. dia.

Cap: pallid olivaceous, or greenish grey, zoned with charac-teristic darker brownish olive spots; at first expanded convex with involute margin, becoming plano–depressed; cuticle glutinous or viscid in wet weather, at first slightly tomentose at the margin, soon wholly glabrous, typically with concentric zonations. Flesh pallid, firm, medium, unchanging, or slightly grey where cut.

Gills: off–white, bruising greyish, or greyish olive, adnate-decurrent, broad, thin, crowded. Spores hyaline, off–white in the mass, sub–spherical, banded–crenulate, 7.5–8.5 μ.

Stipe: pallid greyish, or olivaceous, viscid or glutinous, attenuated downwards. Flesh off–white, at first stuffed, becoming hollow, medium, unchanging or slightly greyish where cut.

All parts yield white latex, finally greying in air.

Inocybe squamata

Lactarius ble

Odour: not distinctive. **Taste:** very acrid.
Occurrence: common. August–November.

Most of the acrid–tasting species of *Lactarius* appear to synthesise poisonous principles which cause, in susceptible individuals, violent stomach pains, vomiting and diarrhoea. It is claimed, however, that the poisons can be removed by boiling in several changes of water. This is a favourite practice on the Continent and explains why many fungi are listed in French and Czechoslovakian food codices which we would not entertain here. The practice is risky, and there is no firm evidence that it always works.

It is advisable, therefore, to leave the *Lactarius* species well alone (with exception of the two listed in the edible section, both of which are thoroughly tried and tested).

LACTARIUS HELVUS (Fr.) Fr.

Habitat: damp, coniferous woods; solitary, or loosely scattered; on soil.

Dimensions: cap 6–10 cm. dia.; stipe 5–8 cm. tall x 1.0–1.5 cm. dia.

Cap: pale yellowish brown, or yellowish café–au–lait, tending to become paler with age; at first convex, becoming expanded, occasionally with slight central umbo, and finally wholly depressed; cuticle squamulose felty or floccose. Flesh paler than cuticle, fragile, thick, unchanging.

Gills: pallid, becoming flesh colour, or concolorous with cap cuticle, but paler; decurrent, broad, crowded, dichotomous. Spores hyaline, cream colour in the mass, sub–globose, inter–rupted–reticulate, 5.5–9.0 x 5.5–6.5 μ.

Stipe: concolorous with cap cuticle, slightly pruinose, and typically tomentose at the base. Flesh at first stuffed, becoming hollow, concolorous, unchanging.

All parts yield scanty white or watery latex, unchanging.

Odour: reminiscent of chicory, or new mown hay, according to different authorities. **Taste:** hardly noticeable, but slightly acrid.

Occurrence: infrequent. September–October.

Lactarius h

LACTARIUS PALLIDUS (Pers. ex Fr.) Fr.

Habitat: mixed woods, favouring beech; solitary, or loosely scattered; on soil.

Dimensions: cap 5–12 cm. dia.; stipe 7–15 cm. tall x 1.5–2.5 cm. dia.

Cap: pale alutaceous, pale tan, or clay colour; at first convex, very soon umbilicate with broadly involute margin, becoming expanded depressed, with involute margin, and finally wholly depressed; cuticle viscid, smooth, glabrous, without zonation. Flesh pallid, firm thick, unchanging.

Gills: concolorous with cap cuticle but paler, or more ochraceous; arcuate–decurrent, broad, thin, crowded, forked. Spores hyaline, pale ochre in the mass, ovate or sub-spherical, crenate–echinate, 8–9 x 5.5–7.0 μ.

Stipe: concolorous with gills, smooth. Flesh stuffed, becoming hollow but firm, concolorous, unchanging.

All parts yield white latex, unchanging.

Odour: not distinctive. **Taste:** at first mild, becoming slightly acrid after chewing.

Occurrence: infrequent. August–November.

LACTARIUS PIPERATUS (Scop. ex Fr.)

Habitat: frondose woods; solitary; on soil.

Dimensions: cap 5–15 cm. dia.; stipe 4–12 cm. tall x 2–3 cm. dia.

Cap: white, tinged creamy yellow in older specimens; at first convex, becoming more plano–depressed, and finally strongly depressed at disc, margin persistently involute; cuticle smooth, glabrous, dull, often showing irregular cracking in older specimens. Flesh white, firm; latex white, unchanging.

Gills: at first white, becoming cream colour at maturity, typically brown spotted when old; decurrent, very crowded, dichotomous (forked). Spores hyaline, cream colour in the mass, ovoid or sub–globose, echinate, 6.0–8.5 x 5.5–6.5 μ.

Stipe: concolorous with cap, stout, attenuated downwards. Flesh white, full, firm.

Odour: not distinctive. **Taste:** extremely acrid.

Occurrence: occasional. August–October.

Lactarius pipere

LACTARIUS PYROGALUS (Bull. ex Fr.) Fr.

Habitat: under hazels; solitary or loosely scattered; on soil.
Dimensions: cap 4–8 cm. dia.; stipe 4–8 cm. tall x 0.5–1.0 cm. dia.
Cap: alutaceous, brownish grey, or violaceous brown grey, becoming distinctly tinged dirty yellow with age; at first convex, becoming expanded; cuticle damp but not truly viscid, typically with slight concentric zonation, smooth, glabrous. Flesh pallid, thin, unchanging.
Gills: light waxy yellow at first, becoming deep ochre yellow; adnate–decurrent, broad, thin, distant, unchanging. Spores yellow, ochre in the mass, ovate or sub–spherical, banded–crenulate, 6.5–9.0 x 5–6 μ.
Stipe: pallid, matt, with some surface sculpturing, attenuated downwards. Flesh concolorous, at first stuffed, soon becoming hollow, unchanging.
Odour: not distinctive. **Taste:** very acrid.
Chemical tests: latex and gills orange with potassium hydroxide.
Occurrence: common. September–October.

LACTARIUS RUFUS (Scop. ex Fr.) Fr.

Habitat: damp, coniferous woods, not recorded on chalk; solitary, or loosely scattered; on soil.
Dimensions: cap 5–9 cm. dia.; stipe 5–7 cm. tall x 1.0–1.5 cm dia.
Cap: rufous, reddish brown, or bay brown; at first umbonate with involute margin, becoming expanded umbonate, to somewhat depressed; cuticle at first minutely floccose tomentose, particularly at the margin, silky, soon becoming smooth, glabrous, polished. Flesh pallid, not compact, unchanging, medium.
Gills: at first pallid ochre, becoming more concolorous with cap cuticle but paler, typically spotted rufous when old; adnate–decurrent, broad, crowded. Spores hyaline, cream colour in the mass, sub–spherical, finely echinate–reticulate, 8–9 x 6–7 μ.
Stipe: concolorous with cap cuticle, but paler; at first minutely pruinose, and for a long time whitely tomentose at the base, becoming wholly smooth and glabrous. Flesh stuffed, fragile, medium, unchanging.
All parts yield white latex, unchanging.
Odour: not distinctive. **Taste:** very acrid and distinctively burning after several seconds on the tongue.
Occurrence: common. August–November.

LACTARIUS TORMINOSUS (Schaeff.) Fr. Woolly milk cap.

Habitat: mixed open woodlands, favouring birch and heath—land; on soil.
Dimensions: cap 5–10 cm. dia.; stipe 4–9 cm. tall x 1–2 cm. dia.
Cap: distinctive alternating concentric zones of cream colour merging with deeper salmon pink or flesh colour; at first convex, becoming expanded and depressed at the disc, but always strongly involute at the margin; cuticle thickly tomentose, although some—what less so with age. Flesh pinkish under cap cuticle, otherwise pallid, medium.
Gills: pallid cream or flesh colour, adnexed, narrow, thin, crowded. Spores hyaline, pallid cream colour in the mass, ovate or spherical, shortly echinate with surface reticulation 8–10 x 6–7 μ.
Stipe: salmon pink beneath cap, becoming more pallid down—wards; wholly glabrous. Flesh concolorous but paler, at first stuffed, becoming hollow and somewhat brittle.
All parts yield milky juice, unchanging.
Odour: said by some authorities to be reminiscent of turpen—tine. **Taste:** very acrid.
Occurrence: common. August–November.

An easy fungus to identify, on account of the extremely woolly appearance from which it gets its popular name and also from the very acrid–tasting juice.

I suspect that should most people eat a cap of *L. torminosus* by mistake it will not cause any serious harm, and the taste is so off–putting that the experience is unlikely to be repeated.

Oddly enough, in certain parts of the Soviet Union and Finland, the fungus is considered a delicacy. It is boiled in several changes of water by the peasants. In Norway they roast the caps, grind them up and add them to coffee, presumably to add a bitter tang. Even so, I believe it is likely to cause indigestion to any but the strongest constitution.

LACTARIUS TURPIS (Weinm.) Fr.

Habitat: birch woods, favouring damp, rich soil; solitary or loosely scattered; on soil.
Dimensions: cap 8–20 cm. dia.; stipe 6–10 cm. tall x 1.5–2.5 cm. dia.
Cap: olivaceous umber, bistre brown, or yellowish olive

Lactarius torminosus

brown, typically more fulvous at the margin; at first convex, becoming expanded with involute margin, and finally somewhat depressed, margin long remaining involute; cuticle viscid, or glutinous in dry weather, typically closely rugose–sulcate, thickly tomentose at the margin, no zonation. Flesh dirty white, soft, thick, unchanging.

Gills: off–white, becoming cream colour, and finally dirty brown at edges; adnate–decurrent, narrow, thick, crowded, forked. Spores hyaline, pallid in the mass, ovate, reticulate, 6.5–7.5 x 5–6 μ.

Stipe: pallid olivaceous brown, viscid or glutinous, attenuated downwards, surface typically sculptured, unchanging. Flesh off–white, full, thick, unchanging.

All parts yield white latex, unchanging.

Odour: not distinctive. **Taste:** very acrid.

Chemical tests: gills violet with potassium hydroxide.

Occurrence: common. August–November.

LACTARIUS VIETUS (Fr.) Fr.

Habitat: under birches; solitary or loosely scattered; on soil, typically damp rich.

Dimensions: cap 3–7 cm. dia.; stipe 4–8 cm. tall x 0.5–1.0 cm dia.

Cap: greyish flesh colour, or greyish brown, typically tinged purple or lilac, becoming paler with age; at first convex becoming expanded to slightly depressed at disc, and finally infundibuliform with partly revolute margin; cuticle at first viscid, becoming more glutinous with age,· smooth, glabrous. Flesh off–white, full, medium, unchanging, or slightly greyish brown, where cut.

Gills: at first off–white or pale greyish, becoming more pale dirty ochre, spotted greyish brown; adnate–decurrent, thin, crowded, flaccid. Spores hyaline, pale olive yellow in the mass, sub–spherical, reticulated–verrucose, 8.0–9.5 x 6.5–7.0 μ.

Stipe: off–white or pale greyish, attenuated upwards, smooth, glabrous, dry. Flesh concolorous, at first stuffed, becoming hollow, but fairly firm, unchanging, or slightly greyish brown where cut.

All parts yield white latex, turning grey in air.

Odour: not distinctive. **Taste:** moderately acrid.

Occurrence: common. August–November.

LEPIOTA CRISTATA (Fr.) Kümmer.

Habitat: typically in light frondose woods along paths, also in grass; in small groups; on soil.
Dimensions: cap 3–4 cm. dis.; stipe 3–5 cm. tall x 0.5–0.75 cm. dia.
Cap: reddish brown; at first campanulate, becoming expanded–umbonate or wholly plane; cuticle broken up into small concentrically arranged scales on pallid background. Flesh off–white, thin.
Gills: whitish, or tinged brown, free, crowded. Spores hyaline, white in the mass, fusiform, smooth, 6.5–9.0 x 2.0–3.5 μ.
Stipe: pale brown, slender, with distant, fugacious annulus, silky fibrillose. Flesh off–white or pallid.
Odour: strongly fungoid.
Occurrence: common. August–October.

Modern knowledge of the toxins synthesised by this fungus is limited, and authenticated reports of poisoning are rare.

However, consumption of *L. cristata* is said to produce effects not unlike mild *Amanita phalloides* poisoning. Mention must be made of it because, although much smaller, the appearance is reminiscent of the edible Lepiotas, and it might be picked by an unsuspecting person thinking it a diminutive or immature *L. rhacodes*.

The most important distinction between the two is that a mature *L. cristata* cap is generally less than half the diameter of that of *L. rhacodes* (or *L. procera*), and the fungus, as a whole, has a far more delicate, membraneous appearance.

L. cristata is the only species of *Lepiota* common in the British Isles which is known to be poisonous.

PAXILLUS INVOLUTUS (Batsch. ex Fr.) Fr.

Habitat: mixed woods, but particularly under birch; solitary or scattered; on soil.
Dimensions: cap 6–12 cm. dia.; stipe 5–7 cm. tall x 1.0–2.5 cm. dia.
Cap: rusty ochre brown, to olive brown; at first planoconvex with strongly involute margin, finally becoming wholly depressed, but long retaining characteristic involute margin; cuticle viscid when damp, otherwise smooth, margin sulcate and at first thickly velvety tomentose. Flesh yellowish brown, soft, full.

Lepiota cris

Paxillus involutus

Gills: pallid at first, discolouring darker where bruised, finally dull olive brown; at first arcuate, becoming more markedly decurrent, broad, crowded, forked. Spores yellowish brown, ovate, smooth, 8–10 x 5–6 μ.

Stipe: dingy yellowish brown, frequently spotted, shorter than cap diameter, attenuated upwards, smooth or finely pruinose. Flesh concolorous, soft, full.

Odour: not distinctive.

Occurrence: very common. August–November.

There is some dispute about the edibility of this fungus, and since, in most seasons, it is extremely common, I prefer to include it among the poisonous species.

It is said to be mildly poisonous when raw, though harmless if cooked, but I suspect that there may be an ageing factor that could produce thermostable toxins.

P. involutus is eaten extensively on the Continent, but I would rather avoid it.

RUSSULA EMETICA (Schaeff. ex Fr.) Gray. The sickener.

Habitat: coniferous woods; scattered; on soil.

Dimensions: cap 5–9 cm. dia.; stipe 5–7 cm. tall x 1.0–1.5 cm. dia.

Cap: at first cerise, becoming scarlet, may be slightly darker at disc; at first hemispherical, becoming convex, and finally plane or slightly depressed; cuticle smooth, glabrous, typically shining, peeling completely, sulcate at the margin. Flesh cap colour beneath cuticle, otherwise white, firm, medium.

Gills: white, unchanging, adnate, fairly narrow, attenuated proximally, distant more or less. Spores hyaline, white in the mass, obtuse, echinate–verrucose with reticular connections, 7.5–9.0 x 7.5–8.5 μ.

Stipe: white, smooth, slightly attenuated upwards. Flesh white, spongy, medium.

Odour: not distinctive. **Taste:** acrid.

Occurrence: common. August–November.

R. emetica, as its name implies, synthesises mildly toxic principles that can cause gastro–enteritis if consumed raw. Since it has a bright colour, and since most of the *Russula* genus are edible, people might be tempted to use it fresh in salads.

Although the toxin(s) are reportedly thermolabile, I think it

Russula emetica

is best left well alone. The taste, like that of *R. queletii* which has similar properties, is distinctly acrid.

RUSSULA MAIREI Singer.

Habitat: typically under beech, but may also occur in mixed woods containing beech; scattered; on soil.

Dimensions: cap 3–6 cm. dia.; stipe 4–5 cm. tall x 1.0–1.5 cm. dia.

Cap: wholly scarlet; at first hemispherical, becoming convex, and finally plane or slightly depressed; cuticle smooth glabrous, peeling to one-third cap diameter. Flesh wholly white, firm, brittle, thin.

Gills: white, unchanging, adnate, fairly narrow, attenuated proximally. Spores hyaline, white in the mass, echinate–verrucose with some reticulation, ovate, 7–8 x 5–6 μ.

Stipe: white, smooth, slightly attenuated upwards. Flesh white, firm, brittle, medium.

Odour: according to Hora, slightly of honey.

Occurrence: common. August–November.

This fungus is reported to be edible, and indeed it does not have the characteristically acrid taste of *R. emetica*. However, its morphological appearance is so similar to the latter species that I prefer to mark it as suspect, if only to avoid the possibility of mistaken identity.

I have found that the assumed restriction to beech woods does not invariably follow, and *R. mairei* can also occur in mixed woods where beech trees are in close proximity. Presumably there is a mycorrhizal association here of an obligate nature.

RUSSULA QUELETII Fr. apud Quél.

Habitat: coniferous woods; scattered; on soil.

Dimensions: cap 3–8 cm. dia.; stipe 3–8 cm. tall x 1.0–2.5 cm. dia.

Cap: purplish red, frequently with violaceous tinge, may be darker at disc, older specimens tinged brownish or brownish olive spotted; at first flatly campanulate, becoming expanded–plane, with slightly flexuose margin, and often bluntly umbonate; cuticle

228

229

Russula mairei

Russula qu

typically slightly viscid in damp weather, otherwise dull, smooth, glabrous, partly separable. Flesh pink beneath cap cuticle, otherwise white, becoming discoloured dirty olive brown where cut.

Gills: white at first, becoming greyish cream colour, ageing with olive brown spots; adnexed–arcuate, attenuated proximally, narrow. Spores cream colour, ovate, strongly spinulose, 8–10 x 7–9 μ.

Stipe: tinged purplish red, smooth or minutely pruinose, slightly attenuated upwards, or mildly clavate at the base. Flesh white, firm, full.

Odour: not distinctive. **Taste:** acrid.

Occurrence: common. August–November.

STROPHARIA AERUGINOSA (Curt. ex Fr.) Quél. Verdigris agaric.

Habitat: woods generally, more prevalent under pines; loosely gregarious; on soil.

Dimensions: cap 3–7 cm. dia.; stipe 4–8 cm. tall x 0.5–1.0 cm. dia.

Cap: verdigris blue–green, discolouring yellowish brown with age; at first campanulate, becoming plano–convex; cuticle viscid, at first covered white floccose, with floccose patches of veil adhering to margin for some time. Flesh pallid greenish blue, firm, medium.

Gills: at first pinkish brown, rapidly becoming dark chocolate colour, adnate, broad. Spores chocolate colour, ellipsoidal, smooth, 7–9 x 4–5 μ.

Stipe: concolorous with cap, but paler, with annulus, at first white floccose; smooth above annulus, squamulose, floccose below. Flesh pallid, fibrillar, medium.

Odour: not distinctive.

Occurrence: common. August–November.

Although a number of authorities on the Continent cite the fungus as being edible, it is generally regarded in this country as suspect, possibly causing gastro–intestinal disorder in allergic individuals.

It is instantly recognisable by the very distinctive colouring and is unlikely to cause confusion with any other species.

Stropharia aerugin

BOLETUS CALOPUS Fr.

Habitat: coniferous woods, but also recorded under frondose trees; singly, on soil.

Dimensions: cap 4–16 cm. dia.; stipe 4–10 cm. tall x 2–4 cm. dia.

Cap: sandy brown, varying to greyish brown, or yellowish olive brown; at first hemispherical, becoming irregularly convex; cuticle dry, at first finely tomentose, becoming glabrescent, margin rounded and extending a little beyond edge of pores. Flesh yellowish, becoming dirty white in older specimens, turning bluish green where cut, thickly fleshy.

Pores: at first dirty white, becoming lemon yellow, and finally greenish, bruising greenish blue; tubes concolorous with pores, sinuate, round, minute. Spores yellowish olive, ellipsoid–fusiform, smooth 12–16 x 4–5 μ.

Stipe: yellowish under cap, otherwise scarlet or tinged purple, covered with distinctive raised venose reticulations, the meshes enlarging towards, and disappearing at, the base; massively ventricose or clavate, but sharply attenuated beneath cap. Flesh off–white to pale cream, turning bluish green where cut, thick, firm, fairly dry.

Odour: not distinctive. **Taste:** at once sweetish but with extremely bitter after–taste.

Occurrence: occasional. August–November.

The fungus is not regarded by any authority as being harm–fully poisonous. However, the very bitter taste can be quite ruinous to a dish of more palatable boleti, hence its inclusion. Easily identifiable on account of the distinctive scarlet stem with its raised white veins. *B. edulis* also has white veins on the stem but differs markedly in that the stipe is never red, and the flesh does not bruise blue.

TYLOPILUS FELLEUS (BOLETUS) *(Bull. ex Fr.) *Karsten. Bitter boletus.

Habitat: coniferous woods, favouring pine and spruce; singly, on soil.

Dimensions: cap 5–12 cm. dia.; stipe 5–12 cm. tall x 2–4 cm. dia.

Cap: light brown, tan, or honey brown; at first convex becoming pulvinate, and finally plano–expanded; cuticle at first

233

minutely tomentose, becoming glabrescent, dry, or slightly viscid in damp weather. Flesh white, except under cap cuticle where stained brownish; thick, at first firm, becoming a little spongy in old specimens; colour unchanging where cut.

Pores: at first off—white or pallid, becoming pale pink, brownish where bruised; tubes deeply sinuate and weakly decurrent, minute, angular, and separable from cap. Spores subhyaline, pale greyish pink in the mass, ellipsoid fusiform, smooth 10–15 x 4–5 μ.

Stipe: at first pallid under cap, becoming more yellowish olive, brownish olive below, covered in darker brown raised venose reticulations; at first ventricose, becoming clavate or subcylindrical. Flesh white, colour unchanging where cut; slightly fibrillar, firm, becoming a little spongy in older specimens.

Odour: not distinctive. **Taste:** extremely bitter, at once.

Occurrence: frequent or common. August–October.

Like *B. calopus,* containing a non-dangerously poisonous but nevertheless extremely bitter principle which can completely spoil a dish of other fungi if inadvertently included. *B. felleus* is chiefly distinguished from *B. edulis* by the pink pores and the dark brown, as opposed to white reticulations on the stem. If these escape you, rest assured that the taste will not!

Appendix

Reference works of Principal Identifying Authorities.

Batsch   Batsch J. G. C. (1783) *Elenchus Fungorum.*
Bolt.   Bolton J. (1788) *History of funguses growing about Halifax.* Halifax.
Boud.   Boudier E. (1905–10) *Icones Mycologicae.* Paris.
Bres.   Bresadola G. (1927–33) *Iconographia Mycologica.* Milan.
Bull.   Bulliard J. (1894) *Herbier de la France. Champignons.* Paris.
Cooke   Cooke M. C. (1881–91) *Illustrations of British fungi.* London.
Corner   Corner E. J. H. (1950) *Clavaria and allied genera.* Oxford.
Dicks.   Dickson J. (1785–1801) *Plantarum Cryptogamicarum Britanniae.* London.
Fr.   Fries E. M. (1867–84) *Icones Selectae Hymenocetae.* Sweden. (Part posthumous publication.)
Gillet   Gillet (1874–78) *Hymenomycetes de France.* Paris.
Kümmer   Kümmer P. (1871) *Der Führer in die Pilzkunde.* Zerbst.
Jacq.   Jacquin A. (1898) *Flore des champignons superieures du department de Saone-et-Loire.* Paris.
Jac.   Jacevski A. A. (1933) *Osnovy mikologii.* Leningrad.
Lange   Lange J. E. (1935–40) *Flora Agaricina Danica.* Copenhagen.
Maire   Maire R. (1902) *Récherches cytologiques et taxonomiques sue les Basidiomycetes.* Paris.
Moser   Moser M. (1955) *Kleine Kryptogamenflora.* Stuttgart.
Pat.   Patouillard (1883–89) *Tabulae Analyticae Fungorum.* Paris.

Pers.	Persoon C. H. (1827–28) *Mycologica Europaea*. Erlangen.
Quél.	Quélet L. (1872–74) *Les Champignons du Jura et Vosges*. Paris.
Ricken	Ricken A. (1923) *Die Blatterpilze*. Leipzig.
Secr.	Secretan L. (1833) *Mycographie Suisse*. Geneva.
Schaeff.	Schaeffer J. (1952) *Russula Monographie. Die Pilze Mittelenropas*. Bad Heilbrunn.
Singer	Singer R. (1962) *The Agaricales in modern taxonomy*. 2nd ed. London.
Sow.	Sowerby J. (1797–1809) *Mycological Illustrations*. London.

Bibliography

ABE M. & YAMATODAMI S. (1964) *Preparation of alkaloids by saprophytic culture of ergot fungi.* Progress in Industrial Micro—biology. 5. (pp. 203–229)

AINSWORTH G. C. & BISBY G. R. (1961) *Dictionary of the. Fungi.* Commonwealth Mycological Institute. Kew.

ALEXOPOULOS C. J. (1963) *Introductory Mycology.* J. Wiley and Sons.

ALLEGRO J. M. (1970) *The Sacred Mushroom and the Cross.* Hodder and Stoughton, London.

ATKINS F. C. (1968) *Mushroom growing today.* Faber and Faber. London.

BADHAM C. D. (1863) *Esculent Funguses of England.* London.

BARGER G. (1931) *Ergot and Ergotism.* Gurney and Jackson. London and Edinburgh.

BENEKE E. S. (1963) *Calvatia, calvacin and cancer.* Mycologia 55. (pp. 257–270)

BESSEY E. A. (1950) *Morphology and Taxonomy of Fungi.* Blakiston. Philadelphia and Toronto.

BULLER A. H. R. (1909) *Researches in Fungi.* London:

BULLER A. H. R. (1915) *The Fungus Lore of Greeks and Romans,* Trans. B. M. C. 38. (pp. 21–66)

BAYLISS–ELLIOT J. S. (1926) *Concerning fairy rings in pastures.* Annals of Applied Biology 13. (pp. 277–288)

CHILD G. P. (1952) *The Inability of Coprini to sensitize man to ethyl alcohol.* Mycologia 44. (pp. 200–202)

COKER W. C. (1951) *The Stipitate Hydnums of Eastern United States.* University of North Carolina Press.

COLSON B. (1935) *The Cytology of the mushroom Psalliota campestris.* Annals Bot. 49. (pp. 1–18)

DARWIN C. (1840) *Journal of Researches during the voyage of HMS Beagle.* Chap. XI. London.

DEARNESS J. (1911) *The Personal Factor in Mushroom Poisoning.* Mycologia 3.

DRAGENDORFF (c. 1898) *Medicinal Plants of the various Peoples and Ages.*

DUBASH J. & TEARE D. (1946) *Poisoning by A. phalloides.* B.M.J. (Jan)

FLOWER B. & ROSENBAUM E. (1958) *The Roman Cookery Book.* Harrap. London.

FORD W. W. (1908) *Pathology of A. phalloides intoxication.* Journal of Infectious Diseases 5. (pp. 115–133)

FORSYTH A. A. (1954) *British Poisonous Plants.* Min. of Ag. Fish and Food Bulletin No. 161. HMSO.

GLEN G. (1816) *A case proving the deleterious effects of Agaricus campanulatus which was mistaken for A. campestris.* London. Medical and Physical Journal 36. (pp. 451–453)

HARTLEY D. M. (1954) *Food in England.* MacDonald. London.

HOUGHTON W. (1885) *Notices of fungi in Greek and Latin authors.* Annals and Magazine of Nat. Hist. ser. 5:5 (pp. 22–49)

INGOLD C. T. (1953) *Dispersal in fungi.* Oxford University Press.

JOCHELSON W. (1906) *Religion and myths of the Koryak in Jesup North Pacific Expedition.* Memoirs of American Museum Nat. Hist.

KAVALER L. (1967) *Mushrooms, moulds and miracles.* Harrap. London.

KRAMER (1928) *Scientific and Applied Pharmacognosy.* J. Wiley and Sons.

LEBEAU J. B. & HAWN E. J. (1963) *Formation of HCN by mycelial stage of fairy ring.*

LOEWENFIELD C. (1956) *Britain's Wild Larder—Fungi.* Faber and Faber. London.

LOWRY B. (1951/2) *A morphological basis for classifying species of Auricularia.* Mycologia 43/44. (pp. 351–358 and 656–692)

LUCAS E. H. (1960) *Folklore & plant drugs.* Michigan Acad. Sc. Arts and Letters 45. (pp. 127–136)

MARSHALL E. M. (1960) *Incidence of certain seed borne diseases in commercial seed samples. II ergot C. purpurea Tul. in cereals.* Annals of Appl. Biol. 48. (pp. 19–26)

PILÁT A. (1954) *Mushrooms.* Bijl. Amsterdam.

PLOWRIGHT C. B. (1879) *A. phalloides poisoning.* Lancet 2 (pp. 941 onwards)

RIVIERE R. D. de la (1933) *Le poison des Amanites mortelles.* Paris.

ROQUES J. (1832) *Histoire des Champignons comestibles et vénéneux.* Paris.

SMITH G. M. (1938) *Cryptogamic Botany* Vol. 1. McGraw Hill. New York.

SIMON A. (1951) *Mushrooms galore.* Newman, Neame.

SOWERBY J. Jun. (1832) *Poisonous fungi resembling mushroom and champignon.* London.

SINGER, SINGER & SMITH (1959) *Hallucinogenics— (teonanácatl) basidiocarps of P. mexicana.* Mycologia 50. (p. 239)

STOLL A. (1945) *les Alcaloides de l'ergot.* Experientia I (pp. 250–262)

TANGHE L. J. & SIMONS D. M. (1973) *Amanita in Eastern United States.* Mycologia 65.

WILDER R. M. & KEYS T. E. (1948) *Foods for emergencies.* Journal of the American Medical Association.

Index to Species

Specific names given in italics; common names in Roman; picture references in boldface.

239